R.D. Spence
Dept of Physics

Nuclear Moments

Nuclear Moments

By

NORMAN F. RAMSEY

Professor of Physics, Harvard University

Reprinted in part from

SEGRÈ (Editor), *Experimental Nuclear Physics*, Vol. I

JOHN WILEY & SONS, INC., NEW YORK
CHAPMAN & HALL, LIMITED, LONDON

Preface

Since 1945 research based upon nuclear moment measurements has increased at a prodigious rate. Before that time almost all the research in this field was done either by optical spectroscopy or by molecular beam methods. Only the molecular beam magnetic resonance method provided high precision in the measurement of nuclear magnetic moments, yet this method was in use only at one laboratory. However, during the past eight years, not only have the earlier methods been improved and more extensively applied, but also a number of entirely new nuclear moment techniques have been developed. They include the methods of microwave spectroscopy and the numerous varieties of nuclear induction or nuclear paramagnetic resonance. As a result, many laboratories are now engaged in nuclear moment measurements.

A field that has grown even more rapidly during this period of time is the application of the methods of nuclear moment measurements to the study of molecular, chemical, liquid, and solid state problems. Until recently there existed only one or two papers primarily devoted to chemical or solid state applications of nuclear moment measurements. There is now an abundant and rapidly increasing literature in this field. The tool of nuclear moment measurements now seems to be one of the most promising and rapidly expanding means for studying chemical and solid state problems.

This book originated from the author's section on "Nuclear Moments and Statistics" in Volume I of *Experimental Nuclear Physics*, edited by E. Segrè. That section was to be concerned only with the aspects of the subject that were predominantly of interest to nuclear physics. Consequently topics that were chiefly of interest to chemistry and solid state physics were suppressed. However, the need for a textbook in this new and rapidly expanding field was so great that a number of the readers of the manuscript urged that it also be published separately so as to be more readily available to chemists and solid state physicists. This book is the response of the author and publishers to this urging.

An extensive new section on applications to chemistry and solid state physics has been written and appears as Section 5. Such a discussion was not relevant to the earlier book on *Experimental Nuclear Physics*, but it should be one of the most valuable parts of this one. It is hoped that this new section will markedly increase the usefulness of the volume

v

both to those whose interests are primarily in chemical and solid state applications and to those who are actively engaged in nuclear moment research and consequently are concerned with all aspects of the subject.

As a result of their origins, the different parts of the book were written at different times, the first four sections having been written in the spring of 1952, and the fifth in the spring of 1953. Also, the references to the original published articles are more extensive and complete for the first four sections than those for the fifth. However, this deficiency should not be serious because references are provided to several review articles in which experimental results relevant to the fifth section are extensively tabulated and lengthy bibliographies are given.

Recently, various nuclear physics techniques, such as the angular correlation of successive gamma-rays, have been successfully applied to the determination of nuclear spins and moments of excited states. However, the techniques of these experiments are so much more closely allied to radioactivity measurements than to those of normal nuclear moment research that it has seemed best to limit this book to stable nuclei and to radioactive nuclei whose lifetimes are sufficiently long for measurements to be possible with techniques that are somewhat similar to those used with stable nuclei. For the experimental methods and results appropriate to excited nuclear states, the reader is referred to the recent review article by B. T. Feld (ZF6).

The first section of this book introduces the subject and defines the quantities concerned in nuclear moment measurements. The second section describes the interaction between nuclear moments and atomic and molecular fields. Many of the nuclear and molecular results described in the subsequent sections depend on the theoretical expressions for the interaction energies derived in the second section. The third section provides a description of the experimental methods used in measuring nuclear moments and the molecular quantities derived therefrom. The fourth section summarizes the results of significance to nuclear physics and the implications of these results in nuclear theory. The discussion of nuclear theory is amplified in somewhat greater detail in the Appendix. The fifth and final section discusses the results of special significance to chemistry and solid state physics.

I wish to express my appreciation to Professors I. I. Rabi, E. M. Purcell, R. V. Pound, F. Bloch, J. H. Van Vleck, J. R. Zacharias, P. Kusch, N. Bloembergen, J. Schwinger, C. Townes, A. Abragam, and the many others who have contributed importantly to this book by extensive discussions with me on many of the topics. I also wish to thank Professor E. Segrè and the contributors to his *Experimental Nuclear*

Physics for their willingness to allow the reprinting of the first four sections. Finally, I wish to express special appreciation to my wife, Elinor Ramsey, and to my secretary, Phyllis Brown, for their extensive help in the preparation of the manuscript.

NORMAN F. RAMSEY

Harvard University
Cambridge, Massachusetts
October, 1953

Contents

1

INTRODUCTION TO NUCLEAR MOMENTS AND
STATISTICS

A. General Characteristics

The gross features of atomic spectra correspond to transitions between the energy levels of electrons moving in the Coulomb field of a positively charged nucleus of negligibly small dimensions. In this case and for Russell-Saunders coupling, the most closely adjacent energy levels are usually those of atomic states which differ in the relative orientation of orbital and electron spin angular momenta. The separation of this "fine structure" varies from less than one-tenth to several thousand wave numbers.

However, if this fine structure is examined more closely, it is often found that each line of the fine structure can in turn be resolved into further lines or "hyperfine structure" with a separation of the order of 1 cm^{-1}. It was first suggested by Pauli (P4) that the hyperfine structure might be due to the action of a magnetic moment of the nucleus on the motion of the electrons.

Since this first suggestion, the effects of nuclear moments have been studied by a number of different methods. However, as will be described in detail subsequently, all observations so far are consistent with the following assumptions concerning atomic nuclei:

(a) A nucleus whose mass number is odd obeys Fermi statistics (the sign of the wave function is reversed if two such identical nuclei are interchanged), and a nucleus whose mass number is even obeys Bose statistics (wave function unaltered on interchange).

(b) A nucleus has a spin angular momentum capable of being represented by a quantum-mechanical angular momentum vector **a** with all the properties [1] usually associated with such vectors. In nuclear moment work it is most convenient to use a dimensionless quantity **I** to measure the angular momentum in units of $\hbar$ where **I** is, therefore, defined by

$$\mathbf{a} = \hbar \mathbf{I} \tag{1}$$

---

[1] A good discussion of the properties of quantized angular momentum vectors is given by Condon and Shortley (C16).

The spin I of the nucleus is defined as the maximum possible component of $\mathbf{I}$ in any given direction.

(c) The nuclear spin I is half-integral if the mass number is odd and integral if the mass number is even.

(d) A nucleus has a magnetic moment $\boldsymbol{\mu}_I$ which can be represented as

$$\boldsymbol{\mu}_I = \gamma_I \hbar \mathbf{I} = g_I \mu_{NM} \mathbf{I} \qquad (2)$$

where γ_I and g_I are defined by the above equations and are called the nuclear gyromagnetic ratio and the nuclear g factor, respectively. μ_{NM} is the nuclear magneton defined as $e\hbar/2Mc$, where M is the proton mass; μ_{NM} has the numerical value 5.04929×10^{-24} erg·gauss^{-1}.[1] The quantity which measures the magnitude of $\boldsymbol{\mu}_I$ and is called the nuclear magnetic moment, μ_I, is

$$\mu_I = \gamma_I \hbar I \qquad (3)$$

With this, Eq. (2) can be written

$$\boldsymbol{\mu}_I = (\mu_I/I)\mathbf{I} \qquad (4)$$

(e) Many nuclei with spin 1 or greater possess an electrical quadrupole moment, i.e., have electrical charge distributions which depart from spherical symmetry in a manner appropriate to an electrical quadrupole moment. (See Section 2 for a precise definition of an electrical quadrupole moment.)

(f) The nucleus instead of being infinitely heavy and of negligibly small dimensions has a finite mass and size. Corrections for these give rise to two different types of isotope shifts that will be discussed in the following sections.

(g) The nucleus has a finite polarizability and can be polarized by a strong electric field (K32, B43, G33).

Values of the above nuclear properties for the different nuclei are given in Section 4. Methods of measuring these properties are given in Section 3. Since many of these methods depend on the interactions of the nuclear moments with the rest of the atom or molecule, these interactions are discussed first in Section 2. Applications of nuclear moment techniques to chemistry and solid state physics are given in Section 5.

---

[1] In the literature of the subject of nuclear moments there is considerable confusion in notation. In some papers μ_0 or μ_n designates the nuclear magneton, whereas in other papers μ_0, μ_1, and β designate the Bohr magneton $e\hbar/2mc$. Here μ_{NM} will be used for the nuclear magneton and μ_0 for the Bohr magneton. Also, in many papers g or g_I is written as above for $\mu_I/(I\mu_{NM})$, but in others g is written for $\mu_I/(I\mu_0)$.

2

INTERACTION OF A NUCLEUS WITH ATOMIC AND MOLECULAR FIELDS

A. Electrostatic Interaction

The general electrostatic interaction between a charged nucleus and the charged electrons and nuclei of the remainder of the atom or molecule is as follows if the finite extension of the nucleus is taken into account:

$$\mathfrak{H}_{el} = + \int_{\tau_e} \int_{\tau_n} \frac{\rho_e(\mathbf{r}_e)\rho_n(\mathbf{r}_n)\, d\tau_e\, d\tau_n}{r} \tag{5}$$

where $\rho_e(r_e)$ is the charge density of the electrons and of the other nuclei in the volume element $d\tau_e$ at position $\mathbf{r}_e$ relative to the center of the nucleus concerned, $\rho_n(r_n)$ is the nuclear charge density of the nucleus concerned in the volume element $d\tau_n$ at position $\mathbf{r}_n$ relative to the center of the nucleus, and r is the magnitude of the radius vector $\mathbf{r}$ joining $d\tau_e$ and $d\tau_n$ as shown in Fig. 1. The definition of $\rho_e(\mathbf{r}_e)$ is such that it is negative for electrons and positive for positive charges.

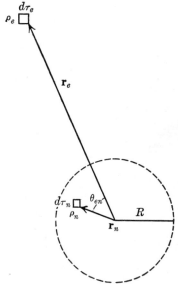

If θ_{en} is the angle between $\mathbf{r}_e$ and $\mathbf{r}_n$ and if r_e is greater than r_n, as may be assured by limiting consideration to electronic charges more distant than the radius R of the nucleus, $1/r$ may be expressed as follows from the cosine law of trigonometry and then expanded

Fig. 1. Electrostatic interactions with nucleus in atoms and molecules.

in the well-known fashion in a power series in r_n/r_e [cf. (M8, p. 96)]:

$$\frac{1}{r} = \frac{1}{\sqrt{r_e{}^2 + r_n{}^2 - 2r_e r_n \cos\theta_{en}}} = \frac{1}{r_e} + \frac{r_n}{r_e{}^2} P_1 + \frac{r_n{}^2}{r_e{}^3} P_2 + \cdots \tag{6}$$

3

where P_l is the Legendre polynomial of $\cos\theta$, so that

$$P_1 = \cos\theta_{en}$$
$$P_2 = \tfrac{1}{2}(3\cos^2\theta_{en} - 1) \tag{7}$$

The term involving P_l is said to arise from the multipole moment of order 2^l. Thus the first term corresponds to a monopole or single charge, the second to the electric dipole moment, and the third to the electric quadrupole moment.

The first term is the one already used in normal atomic theory and consequently is of no interest in a discussion of nuclear moments. The second term, corresponding to an electrical dipole moment, should be zero for reasons of symmetry to be discussed shortly and has indeed been experimentally found to be zero for all nuclei so far studied. Electric moments higher than electrical quadrupole moments have so far been too small to be observed. Consequently, in the study of nuclear moments the only important electrostatic term is the quadrupole one. If the above equations are combined in evaluating the interaction energy, functions of the cosine of the angle θ between $\mathbf{r}_n$ and $\mathbf{r}_e$ must be integrated over all directions of $\mathbf{r}_n$ and of $\mathbf{r}_e$. This might lead one to expect a very complicated result. However, as shown in Section 2C, if full advantage is taken of the symmetry properties of the nucleus, the electrostatic quadrupole interaction term reduces to (C5, C6, K8)

$$\mathfrak{H}_Q = \frac{e^2 q_J Q}{2I(2I-1)J(2J-1)}\left[3(\mathbf{I}\cdot\mathbf{J})^2 + \frac{3}{2}\mathbf{I}\cdot\mathbf{J} - \mathbf{I}^2\mathbf{J}^2\right] \tag{8}$$

where Q is the single arbitrary nuclear constant required to describe the quadrupole interaction and is called the magnitude of the electrical quadrupole moment and is defined by

$$eQ \equiv \int \rho_n(\mathbf{r}_n)_{m_I=I}(3z_n^2 - r_n^2)\,d\tau_n \tag{9}$$

where the subscript indicates the integral is carried out for the nuclear state whose magnetic quantum number $m_I = I$. Q has the dimension of square centimeters. Since $\rho_n(\mathbf{r}_n)$ is proportional to the nuclear charge Z, this definition of Q (which is the conventional one) carries an implicit factor of Z, e.g., if two nuclei were of the same size and shape their quadrupole moments would be proportional to their nuclear charges Z. Likewise

$$eq_J \equiv \int_{r_e>R} \rho_e(\mathbf{r}_e)_{m_J=J}(3\cos^2\theta_{ez} - 1)\frac{1}{r_e^3}\,d\tau_e \tag{10}$$

where θ_{ez} is the angle between $\mathbf{r}_e$ and the z axis relative to which this state has $m_J = J$ and where it usually is possible to allow $R \to 0$ after the integration is completed. In the classical limit of large I and J, Eq. (8) reduces to the more familiar classical expression

$$\mathfrak{H}_Q = \frac{e^2 q_J Q}{4} \frac{1}{2} (3 \cos^2 \theta_{IJ} - 1) = \frac{e^2 q_J Q}{4} P_2(\cos \theta_{IJ}) \qquad (11)$$

where θ_{IJ} is the angle between $\mathbf{I}$ and $\mathbf{J}$. The $\mathbf{I} \cdot \mathbf{J}$ term in Eq. (8) is purely a quantum-mechanical one corresponding to the fact that the quantum-mechanical analogue of $\cos^2 \theta$ is not $(\mathbf{I} \cdot \mathbf{J})^2 / \mathbf{I}^2 \mathbf{J}^2$.

Although the above form for the quadrupole interaction is the one most frequently used in discussions of the quadrupole interaction in atoms, it is less suited to treatment of quadrupole interactions in linear $^1\Sigma$ molecules. This arises from the fact that q_J, as indicated by the subscript J, for $^1\Sigma$ molecules is dependent on the magnitude of the rotational quantum number J of the molecule. This dependence results from the state $m_J = J$ having its $\mathbf{J}$ much more nearly parallel to the z axis when J is large than when J is small. For discussions of such molecules it is, therefore, desirable to re-express Eq. (8) in a form such that all the J dependence is explicitly indicated. As shown in Section 2C, this can be done by replacing q_J by

$$q_J = -\frac{J}{2J + 3} \frac{1}{e} \frac{\partial^2 V^e}{\partial z_0^2} \qquad (12)$$

where V^e is the potential from the charges external to a small sphere surrounding the nucleus (as emphasized by the superscript e) and z_0 is along the axis of symmetry of the molecule.[1] With this replacement Eq. (8) becomes

$$\mathfrak{H}_Q = -\frac{eQ(\partial^2 V^e / \partial z_0^2)}{2I(2I - 1)(2J + 3)(2J - 1)} \left[3(\mathbf{I} \cdot \mathbf{J})^2 + \frac{3}{2} \mathbf{I} \cdot \mathbf{J} - \mathbf{I}^2 \mathbf{J}^2 \right]$$

$$(13)$$

Although this equation is applicable only to linear molecules, it can easily be modified to apply to symmetrical top molecules, as done in Section 2C and as discussed in greater detail in Section 3G.

---

[1] There is much notational confusion in the literature on this point. Kellogg, Rabi, Ramsey, and Zacharias (K8) use the symbol q for what is here called q_J. Bardeen and Townes (B4), on the other hand, use q to represent the quantity here represented by $\partial^2 V^e / \partial z_0^2$, and Feld (F7) and others use $\partial^2 V / \partial z^2$ for this quantity. Also, Nordsieck (N11) and Ramsey (R11) have sometimes used the still different quantity q', which is related to the above by $\varrho' = (1/2e)(\partial^2 V^e / \partial z_0^2)$.

When the interaction between the vectors $\mathbf{I}$ and $\mathbf{J}$ is large compared to the interaction of either with any other field, Eq. (13) can be expressed in an alternative form. Let the angular momentum which is the vector sum of $\mathbf{I}$ and $\mathbf{J}$ be $\mathbf{F} = \mathbf{I} + \mathbf{J}$ with quantum number F. Then $\mathbf{I} \cdot \mathbf{J}$ can be evaluated from

$$\mathbf{F}^2 = (\mathbf{I} + \mathbf{J})^2 = \mathbf{I}^2 + \mathbf{J}^2 + 2\mathbf{I} \cdot \mathbf{J} \tag{14}$$

so

$$\mathbf{I} \cdot \mathbf{J} = \tfrac{1}{2}(\mathbf{F}^2 - \mathbf{I}^2 - \mathbf{J}^2) = \tfrac{1}{2}[F(F+1) - I(I+1) - J(J+1)] \equiv \tfrac{1}{2}C \tag{15}$$

This can be used in Eq. (13), whence the quadrupole energy E_Q is

$$E_Q = - \frac{eQ(\partial^2 V^e/\partial z_0^2)}{I(2I-1)(2J+3)(2J-1)}$$
$$\times [\tfrac{3}{8}C(C+1) - \tfrac{1}{2}I(I+1)J(J+1)] \tag{16}$$

The above electrical quadrupole interaction occurs in general along with various magnetic interactions often of comparable magnitude. Consequently the determination of the energy levels in most actual problems depends on solving a secular equation of a matrix of a Hamiltonian one of whose terms is similar to the above. Therefore in the solution of most problems both the diagonal and non-diagonal matrix elements of the above interaction must be evaluated. This can be done from Eq. (61). Alternatively, a table evaluating these has been published by Kellogg, Rabi, Ramsey, and Zacharias (K8), and it is often of value in actual problems. Their paper also provides a detailed example of the application of the above quadrupole interaction expressions to a practical problem, the evaluation of the quadrupole moment of the deuteron.

In order that the electrical quadrupole moment Q may be experimentally determined from the observed interaction energy, it is necessary according to Eq. (8) or (13) to have a determination of the atomic or molecular constant q_J or $\partial^2 V^e/\partial z_0^2$. Various methods for estimating these quantities have been devised. For many atoms, q_J can be evaluated (C5, K29) in terms of the experimentally measured fine structure constant for the atom, since the latter, like q_J, is also dependent on the mean value of $1/r_e^3$. Illustrative of such results is the following value of q_J which applies when q_J is due to a single electron in a $^2P_{3/2}$ state:

$$q_J = \frac{2}{5} \frac{\delta}{\mu_0^2 Z_i} \eta \tag{17}$$

where δ is the experimentally observed optical fine (not hyperfine) structure separation, Z_i is the effective nuclear charge introduced by Landé (L2, W8) into the theory of fine structure, and η is a correction factor which is approximately unity and is evaluated by Casimir (C6). Recently Davis, Feld, Zabel, and Zacharias (D7) in studies of atomic chlorine have used their experimentally observable magnetic hyperfine structure splitting and the known nuclear magnetic moment to determine the mean value of $1/r_e^3$ as discussed subsequently in Sections 2B and 2E. With this determination and the assumption of the separability of the angular and radial electron wave function, q_J is directly determined and can be combined with their own determination of the quadrupole interaction of the same atom to yield the value of the nuclear quadrupole moment. This measurement is particularly direct and effective since it does not depend on such correction factors as Z_i and η. However, it has recently been pointed out by Sternheimer (S46) that the inner electron shells of an atom partially shield the nucleus from the gradient of the electric field from the outer charged particles. Consequently, gradients calculated from the latter alone are likely to be in error by approximately 4 to 45 percent and thus lead to errors in the measured quadrupole moments of this amount. Sternheimer's correction, however, does not apply to the quadrupole moment of the deuteron since in this case the effects of all the electrons are included in the calculation. However, the measurements of all other nuclear quadrupole moments have an uncertainty due to this phenomenon.

In the important case of molecular D_2, Nordsieck (N11) and Newell (N7) have directly calculated q_J from the molecular wave function. Extension of this method to other molecules is numerically quite difficult. However, Townes (T22) has suggested for heavy atoms covalently bonded in molecules with p-orbitals that $\partial^2 V^e/\partial z_0^2$ can be calculated from atomic fine structure separations in the same way as from atomic spectra, as discussed in much greater detail in Section 5B.

From Eq. (5) it might appear that an electric multipole moment of order 2^l would be possible for any integral value of l greater than or equal to zero. However, by quite general arguments it can be shown that the orders of the possible multipoles are considerably restricted. The proofs of these restrictions are given in Section 2D, and the results only are summarized immediately below. Provided that the nuclear states are not degenerate in I, provided that all electrical effects arise from electrical charges, and provided that nuclear forces conserve parity, all odd (l odd) electric multipole moments vanish. This is the theorem used above to justify omitting electric dipole moments from consideration. The proof in Section 2D is essentially the same as in the atomic case (V1) and depends on the parity properties of the wave functions. In the nuclear case there is no reason to expect a degeneracy of levels (as in the hydrogen *atom*) which would give rise to exceptions to the general rule, since the energy separations of the different nuclear energy levels are in general very large compared to any of electric interaction energies within the atoms or molecules. However, Purcell and Ramsey (P28) have recently pointed out that this proof depends on the assumption that the electrical effects of a nucleus arise only from electrical charges or a related parity assumption and that these assumptions are not necessarily self-obvious in the case of little-understood particles like nucleons and nuclei. They have, therefore, searched with high precision for an electrical dipole moment for the neutron. In an experiment with J. Smith, they find (S45) that, if such a dipole moment exists, its magnitude must be less than the charge on the electron multiplied by a distance $D = 5 \times 10^{-21}$ cm.

In addition to the above restriction on l it may be shown, as in Section 2D,[1] that for a nuclear spin of I it is impossible to observe a multipole moment of order 2^l greater than that corresponding to $l = 2I$. In other words, for a quadrupole moment to be observable the spin must be at least $I = 1$. This result is very reasonable indeed, for, if the spin were $\frac{1}{2}$ and the nuclear charge distribution were spheroidal in shape with the spin axis being the spheroid's axis of symmetry, the quadrupole moment would still be experimentally undetectable since only two values for m_I of $\pm\frac{1}{2}$ are allowed and for these two the charge distribution is essentially the same. Similar restrictions to the above apply to the angular momentum of the atom with which the nuclear multipole moment interacts. Thus, if J is less than 1, an electric quadrupole interaction with a nucleus will not show up experimentally even though the nucleus may have a large electric quadrupole moment.

There is one electrostatic effect in atoms which is often experimentally important even though it is not directly concerned with nuclear moments. This is the so-called isotope shift of heavy nuclei. As stated earlier, the expansion in Eq. (6) is valid only if $r_e > r_n$; it is incorrect to assume the simple $1/r_e$ dependence for the spherically symmetric term of Eq. (6) for $r_e < R$, the nuclear radius. Approximate calculations of the shift produced by this effect of the finite size of the nucleus have been made (B36, R8, K29). This effect is particularly important with penetrating outer orbits and heavy nuclei. With heavy elements, since different isotopes of the same element have nuclei of slightly different size, the effect is different for different isotopes. This is the origin

---

[1] An alternative simple proof based on the Hamilton-Cayley equation is given by Nierenberg *et al.* (N9).

of its name, isotope shift. Recently Fierz (F9a), Brix (B44), Kopfermann (K32, B44), Breit (B43), A. Bohr (B30), and others have suggested that studies of the isotope shift may yield valuable information about nuclear charge distribution and perhaps about the polarization of nuclei by atomic electrons since the electrical polarizabilities of the isotopes may be different.

B. Magnetic Interaction

The magnetic interaction of a nucleus, with its associated atom or molecule and with any externally applied magnetic field, can be expanded in a multipole series closely analogous to Eq. (6). Also, analogous parity and angular momentum arguments apply to limit the allowed multipole orders 2^l. For magnetic multipole moments the limitations are that l must be odd and l must be less than or equal to $2I$, where I is the spin of the nucleus concerned.

The lowest order of magnetic interaction is therefore magnetic dipole, the next higher being magnetic octupole. So far no magnetic octupole or higher magnetic multipole interaction has been definitely observed. Tolansky (T13) has suspected octupole effects in iodine. However, Casimir and Karreman (C8) have developed a detailed theory of magnetic octupole interactions. They find that an unreasonably large octupole moment would be required to give Tolansky's results. Consequently consideration of magnetic interactions will here be limited to magnetic dipole moments for which the interaction energy is

$$\mathfrak{H}_M = -\mathbf{\mu}_I \cdot (\mathbf{H}_J + \mathbf{H}_0) \tag{18}$$

where $\mathbf{\mu}_I$ is the nuclear magnetic moment, $\mathbf{H}_0$ the externally applied magnetic field, and $\mathbf{H}_J$ the magnetic field at the nucleus arising from the rest of the atom or molecule which has angular momentum $\mathbf{J}$ in units of $\hbar$. This form of magnetic interaction implies the assumption that the electron current distribution inside the nucleus does not contribute appreciably to the interaction energy. It can be shown (C6, B29) that this contribution is only a few percent even in the worst case —heavy nuclei and S electrons.

As stated in Section 1, the magnetic moment vector of a nucleus can be taken (C16, W10, P5) as proportional to its spin angular momentum, which proportionality can be written as

$$\mathbf{\mu}_I = \left(\frac{\mu_I}{I}\right)\mathbf{I} \tag{19}$$

with the notation of Section 1.

From Eqs. (18) and (19) the magnetic interaction energy may be written

$$\mathfrak{H}_M = -\left(\frac{\mu_I}{I}\right)\mathbf{I}\cdot(\mathbf{H}_J + \mathbf{H}_0) \qquad (20)$$

If $\mathbf{H}_J$ is zero, as in S states or $^1\Sigma$ states of non-rotating molecules, μ_I may readily be evaluated from a measurement of the energy levels, from a knowledge of the applied field $\mathbf{H}_0$, and from Eq. (20). However, in other atoms where the contribution of $\mathbf{H}_J$ is important it is necessary to evaluate $\mathbf{H}_J$ theoretically. Just as $\boldsymbol{\mu}_I$ in Eq. (19) above could be taken as proportional to $\mathbf{I}$, so here $\mathbf{H}_J$ can be taken as proportional to $\mathbf{J}$ for matrix elements diagonal in J, so that, if the external field $\mathbf{H}_0$ is zero, Eq. (20) becomes

$$\mathfrak{H}_M = a\mathbf{I}\cdot\mathbf{J} \qquad (21)$$

where a contains all the proportionality constants and is defined by

$$a = -\left(\frac{\mu_I}{I}\right)\frac{\mathbf{H}_J}{\mathbf{J}} = -\left(\frac{\mu_I}{I}\right)\frac{\mathbf{H}_J\cdot\mathbf{J}}{\mathbf{J}\cdot\mathbf{J}} \qquad (22)$$

The value of $\mathbf{I}\cdot\mathbf{J}$ obtained in Eq. (15) may be used here with the result that

$$\mathfrak{H}_M = \frac{a}{2}[F(F + 1) - I(I + 1) - J(J + 1)] \qquad (23)$$

In order that g_I may be experimentally determined from the energy levels it is necessary according to Eqs. (23) and (22) to have an estimate for $\mathbf{H}_J$, the effective magnetic field at the nucleus due to the rest of the atom. For hydrogen-like atoms this effective field has been calculated by Fermi, Goudsmit, and others (F8, G18, K29). A simplified version of these calculations is given in Section 2E. The results are that for an S electron

$$a = \frac{16\pi}{3}\,\mu_0\,\frac{\mu_I}{I}\,|\,\psi_{n0}(0)\,|^2 = \frac{8}{3}\frac{2\pi\hbar c\,\text{Ry}\,\alpha^2 Z^3 g_I}{n^3(M/m)} \qquad (24)$$

and for an electron of orbital angular momentum $L \neq 0$

$$a = \frac{2\pi\hbar c\,\text{Ry}\,\alpha^2 Z^3 g_I}{n^3(L + \frac{1}{2})J(J + 1)(M/m)} \qquad (25)$$

where Ry is the Rydberg constant $(2\pi^2 me^4/h^3 c\ \text{cm}^{-1})$, α is the fine structure constant $e^2/(\hbar c)$, M/m is the ratio of the proton to the electron mass, and $\psi_{n0}(0)$ is the wave function of the electron at the position of zero radius. Small corrections to the above have been introduced by Breit (B32, B41, B42) and Margenau (M9) to allow for the reduced mass effect of the nucleus and for the relativistic effects of the atomic electron. The reduced mass effect introduces an extra factor of $(1 + m/M)^{-3}$ into Eq. (24). Low and Salpeter (L10b) have recently introduced a small additional reduced mass correction corresponding to recoil of the nucleus from the virtual photons that are interchanged. An approximate formula for the calculation of the interaction constant in alkali metals has been calculated by Goudsmit (G19) and is identical with Eq. (25) except that Z^3 is replaced by $Z_0{}^2Z_i$ and n is replaced by n_0, where Z_i is the effective charge when the valence electron is inside the core of closed electron shells, Z_0 is the effective charge when it is outside the core, and n_0 is the effective principal quantum number outside the core. Therefore, for alkali atoms,

$$a = \frac{2\pi\hbar c \; \mathrm{Ry} \; \alpha^2 Z_0{}^2 Z_i(\mu_I/I\mu_{NM})}{n_0{}^3(L + \tfrac{1}{2})J(J + 1)(M/m)} \tag{26}$$

If the fine structure separation δ of the same term is known, it can be used empirically to eliminate the Z_0 and n_0 dependence, since by atomic theory

$$\delta = \frac{2\pi\hbar c \; \mathrm{Ry} \; \alpha^2 Z_0{}^2 Z_i{}^2}{n_0{}^3 L(L + 1)} \tag{27}$$

so

$$a = \frac{\delta L(L + 1)}{(L + \tfrac{1}{2})J(J + 1)Z_i(M/m)} \tag{28}$$

Various corrections to Eq. (26) have been calculated by Fermi and Segrè (F9), Breit (B34), Racah (R7), Goudsmit and Bacher (G17) and Wills (B37), and the results have been summarized by Kopfermann (K29). In addition to the relation (26) applying for alkali atoms with 1 valence electron, it can also be used for halogens where just 1 electron is missing from the outer shell. It can further be applied approximately to atoms of the aluminum group, since the first two valence electrons form a more or less closed shell. More complicated relationships hold for 2 valence electrons such as alkaline earths. These have been summarized by Kopfermann (K29).

All the states of a single hyperfine structure group have the same values of the quantum numbers I and J in Eq. (23) while F takes on values from $I + J$ to $|I - J|$. The energy difference between a state with $F = F$ and $F = F - 1$ is, according to Eq. (23),

$$\mathfrak{H}_M(F) - \mathfrak{H}_M(F - 1) = aF \tag{29}$$

This regularity is called the interval rule, and for this reason a is often called the interval factor. However, even with magnetic dipole interactions, exceptions to this rule can occur if two atomic states of different J are separated by an amount which is not large compared to the hyperfine structure, in which case J in Eq. (23) is no longer a good quantum number and second-order perturbations must be taken into account. Calculations of the effect of perturbations have been made by Fermi and Segrè, Casimir, Goudsmit, and Bacher (F9, C4, G20).

If $J = \frac{1}{2}$, the separation, $2\pi\hbar\,\Delta\nu$, of the hyperfine structure levels is

$$2\pi\hbar\,\Delta\nu = aF = a\left(I + \frac{1}{2}\right) = a\,\frac{2I + 1}{2} \tag{30}$$

The quantity $\Delta\nu$ defined in this way is frequently referred to as the hyperfine structure separation, or the hfs $\Delta\nu$.

So far in the detailed discussion of Eq. (20) it has been assumed either that there was no intramolecular interaction or that the external magnetic field was zero. However, in many of the practical cases which arise in nuclear moment measurements the magnetic interactions of the electrons and the nuclei with each other and of one or both with the external field are of comparable importance.

The effect of an external magnetic field on the hyperfine structure of a spectral line illustrates such a combined interaction. In this case, if the interaction energy of the electrons as well as the nucleus with external magnetic field is included, and if μ_J is the resultant electronic magnetic moment defined analogously to Section 1, Eqs. (20) and (22) become

$$\mathfrak{H}_M = a\,\mathbf{I}\cdot\mathbf{J} - \frac{\mu_J}{J}\,\mathbf{J}\cdot\mathbf{H}_0 - \frac{\mu_I}{I}\,\mathbf{I}\cdot\mathbf{H}_0 \tag{31}$$

If the magnetic field is very weak, corresponding to a weak field Zeeman effect, the term $a\,\mathbf{I}\cdot\mathbf{J}$ in the above is the largest, so that $\mathbf{I}$ and $\mathbf{J}$ are tightly coupled together to form a resultant $\mathbf{F}$ as in Fig. 2. As a consequence, only the components of the electron and nuclear magnetic moments along $\mathbf{F}$ are effective, since the perpendicular components average to zero and the above becomes approximately

$$\mathfrak{H}_M = a\,\mathbf{I}\cdot\mathbf{J} - \frac{\mu_J}{J}\,\mathbf{J}\cdot\frac{\mathbf{F}}{|\mathbf{F}|}\frac{\mathbf{F}}{|\mathbf{F}|}\cdot\mathbf{H}_0 \tag{32}$$

where the nuclear moment's interaction with the external field is neg-

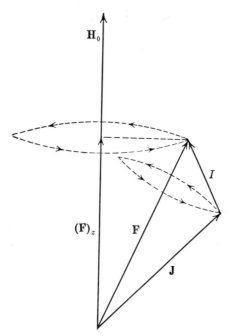

Fig. 2. Coupling of nuclear angular momentum **I** and electronic angular momentum **J** in weak magnetic field $\mathbf{H}_0$.

lected because of the small size of both the nuclear moment and the field. But

$$\mathbf{I} \cdot \mathbf{I} = (\mathbf{F} - \mathbf{J}) \cdot (\mathbf{F} - \mathbf{J}) = |\mathbf{F}|^2 + |\mathbf{J}|^2 - 2\mathbf{J} \cdot \mathbf{F} \qquad (33)$$

so the energy for the state specified by quantum numbers F and m, where m is the magnetic quantum number for F, is

$$
\begin{aligned}
W_M(F, m) &= (F, m| \, \mathfrak{H}_M \, |F, m) \\
&= a(F, m| \, \mathbf{I} \cdot \mathbf{J} \, |F, m) \\
&\quad - \frac{\mu_J}{J} \frac{[F(F + 1) + J(J + 1) - I(I + 1)]}{2F(F + 1)} \\
&\quad \times (F, m| \, \mathbf{F} \cdot \mathbf{H}_0 \, |F, m) \\
&= \frac{a}{2}[F(F + 1) - I(I + 1) - J(J + 1)] \\
&\quad - \frac{\mu_J}{J} \frac{[F(F + 1) + J(J + 1) - I(I + 1)]}{2F(F + 1)} H_0 m \qquad (34)
\end{aligned}
$$

In the limit of a very strong magnetic field corresponding to a Paschen-Back effect, on the other hand, I and J will each separately precess rapidly about H as in Fig. 3, so that F is no longer a good quan-

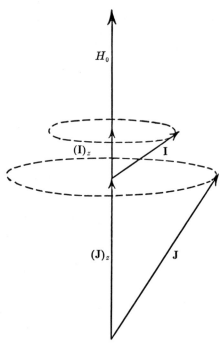

Fig. 3. Coupling of nuclear angular momentum I and electronic angular momentum J in strong magnetic field $\mathbf{H}_0$.

tum number but instead the good quantum numbers are the magnetic quantum numbers, m_I and m_J, of I and J separately.

Then from Eq. (31)

$$W_M(m_I, m_J) = (m_I m_J | \, \mathfrak{H}_m \, | m_I m_J)$$

$$= a(m_I m_J | \, (\mathbf{I})_x(\mathbf{J})_x + (\mathbf{I})_y(\mathbf{J})_y + (\mathbf{I})_z(\mathbf{J})_z \, | m_I m_J)$$

$$- \frac{\mu_J}{J} H m_J - \frac{\mu_I}{I} H m_I$$

$$= - \frac{\mu_J}{J} H m_J - \frac{\mu_I}{I} H m_I + a m_I m_J \tag{35}$$

since the diagonal elements of I_x and I_y are zero.

The case of intermediate coupling is of particular importance in nuclear moment research, even though it is more difficult to work out the energy levels since a secular equation must be solved as in the corresponding fine structure case (C16). The result of a straightforward solution of the secular equation in the case $J = \frac{1}{2}$ and for any I is (B35, M17)

$$W_M(F, m) = -\frac{\Delta W}{2(2I+1)} - \frac{\mu_I}{I}Hm \pm \frac{\Delta W}{2}\sqrt{1 + \frac{4m}{2I+1}x + x^2} \quad (36)$$

where

$$\Delta W \equiv \frac{a}{2}(2I+1) \equiv 2\pi\hbar\,\Delta\nu \qquad x = \frac{(-\mu_J/J + \mu_I/I)H}{\Delta W} \quad (37)$$

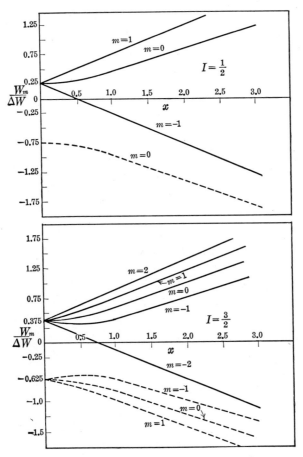

Fig. 4. Variation of the energy with the magnetic field. Nuclear moment assumed positive. The dotted lines are the magnetic levels arising from the $F = I - \frac{1}{2}$ state (R4).

and the $+$ is used for $F = I + \frac{1}{2}$ and the $-$ for $F = I - \frac{1}{2}$. This energy dependence for the case of $I = \frac{1}{2}$ and $\frac{3}{2}$ is plotted in Fig. 4. The quantity $\Delta\nu$ is the "hyperfine structure $\Delta\nu$" or the hyperfine structure separation of Eq. (30).

C. Appendix A. Form of Nuclear Electrical Quadrupole Moment Interaction

From Eqs. (5) and (6),

$$\mathfrak{H}_Q = \int_{\tau_e} \int_{\tau_n} r_n{}^2 \rho_n(\mathbf{r}_n) \frac{1}{2} (3\cos^2\theta_{en} - 1) \frac{\rho_e{}^e(\mathbf{r}_e)}{r_e{}^3} d\tau_n\, d\tau_e \qquad (38)$$

The superscript e is used to indicate the charge density *external* to the nucleus concerned, since the expansion is valid only for $r_e > r_n$. The above can readily be expanded in Cartesian coordinates by use of the relation that $r_n r_e \cos\theta_{en}$ equals $\sum_i x_{ni} x_{ei}$. With this expansion Eq. (38) becomes

$$\mathfrak{H}_Q = \int_{\tau_e} \int_{\tau_n} \rho_n(\mathbf{r}_n) \left[\frac{3}{2} \sum_{ij} x_{ni} x_{nj} x_{ei} x_{ej} - \frac{1}{2} r_n{}^2 r_e{}^2 \right] \frac{\rho_e{}^e(\mathbf{r}_e)}{r_e{}^3} d\tau_n\, d\tau_e$$

On the other hand, if Eq. (39) below is directly expanded with the first form of Eq. (40) and the second form of Eq. (41), the same equation is also obtained. Therefore, Eq. (38) can be expressed in the alternative tensor form

$$\mathfrak{H}_Q = -\tfrac{1}{6} \sum_{ij} Q_{ij} (\nabla \mathbf{E}^e)_{ij} \qquad (39)$$

where

$$Q_{ij} = \int_{\tau_n} \rho_n(\mathbf{r}_n)(3x_{ni}x_{nj} - \delta_{ij} r_n{}^2)\, d\tau_n$$

$$= \int_{\tau_n} \rho_n(\mathbf{r}_n)(3\, \frac{x_{ni}x_{nj} + x_{nj}x_{ni}}{2} - \delta_{ij} r_n{}^2)_n \qquad (40)$$

and

$$(\nabla \mathbf{E}^e)_{ij} = -\int_{\tau_e} \rho_e{}^e(\mathbf{r}_e) \frac{\partial}{\partial x_i} \frac{\partial}{\partial x_j} \left(\frac{1}{r_e}\right) d\tau_e$$

$$= -\int_{\tau_e} \frac{\rho_e{}^e(\mathbf{r}_e)}{r_e{}^5} (3x_{ei}x_{ej} - \delta_{ij} r_e{}^2)\, d\tau_e$$

$$= -\int_{\tau_e} \frac{\rho_e{}^e(\mathbf{r}_e)}{r_e{}^5} (3\, \frac{x_{ei}x_{ej} + x_{ej}x_{ei}}{2} - \delta_{ij} r_e{}^2)\, d\tau_e \qquad (41)$$

The final forms above of Eqs. (40) and (41) arise from the fact that the components of $\mathbf{r}$ commute among themselves ($x_i x_j = x_j x_i$), whence the tensors are symmetric; this manner of writing explicitly exhibits the symmetric character of the tensor. It is also immediately apparent that the traces (diagonal sums) of Eqs. (40) and (41) are zero.

The next step of the proof is most simply taken from group theory. However, it may also be shown directly from simple matrix multiplications. Since the latter proof, though numerically tedious, is conceptually simpler and is not conveniently available in the published literature, it is outlined in the addendum on page 21. This proof also automatically provides a numerical evaluation of the quantum-mechanical matrix elements of the quadrupole interaction. The theorem which can be proved either by group theory (W14) or as in the addendum applies to all second-rank tensors of, say, the form (40) which (a) are constructed in the same manner from vectors satisfying the same commutation rules with respect to $\mathbf{I}$, (b) are symmetric, and (c) have a zero trace. This theorem states that the quantum-mechanical matrix elements diagonal in I of all such tensors have the same dependence on the magnetic quantum number m_I.

The above theorem shows that, as concerns the m_I dependence of matrix elements $(Im| Q_{ij} |Im')$ diagonal in I of Eq. (40), Q_{ij} may be replaced by

$$Q_{ij} = C \left[3 \frac{(\mathbf{I})_i(\mathbf{I})_j + (\mathbf{I})_j(\mathbf{I})_i}{2} - \delta_{ij}I^2 \right] \qquad (42)$$

since this tensor satisfies the above three conditions. The arbitrary constant C can be expressed in terms of the scalar quantity Q, which is conventionally called the nuclear quadrupole moment and is defined by

$$Q \equiv \frac{1}{e} \int \rho_{nm_I = I} [3z_n^2 - r_n^2] \, d\tau_n = (II| Q_{33} |II)$$

$$= C(II| 3(\mathbf{I})_z^2 - \mathbf{I}^2 |II) = C[3I^2 - I(I + 1)]$$

$$= CI(2I - 1) \qquad (43)$$

Hence

$$Q_{ij} = \frac{eQ}{I(2I - 1)} \left[3 \frac{(\mathbf{I})_i(\mathbf{I})_j + (\mathbf{I})_j(\mathbf{I})_i}{2} - \delta_{ij}I^2 \right] \qquad (44)$$

Likewise, for matrix elements diagonal in J,

$$(\nabla \mathbf{E}^e)_{ij} = - \frac{eq_J}{J(2J - 1)} \left[3 \frac{(\mathbf{J})_i(\mathbf{J})_j + (\mathbf{J})_j(\mathbf{J})_i}{2} - \delta_{ij}J^2 \right] \qquad (45)$$

where

$$q_J = \frac{1}{e} \int \frac{3z_e^2 - r_e^2}{r_e^5} \rho_{e,m_J = J} \, d\tau_e \qquad (46)$$

Therefore

$$\mathfrak{H}_Q = \frac{1}{6}\frac{e^2 q_J Q}{I(2I-1)J(2J-1)} \sum_{ij}\left[3\frac{(\mathbf{I})_i(\mathbf{I})_j + (\mathbf{I})_j(\mathbf{I})_i}{2} - \delta_{ij}\mathbf{I}^2\right]$$

$$\times\left[3\frac{(\mathbf{J})_i(\mathbf{J})_j + (\mathbf{J})_j(\mathbf{J})_i}{2} - \delta_{ij}\mathbf{J}^2\right] \quad (47)$$

Equation (47) can be expressed in an alternative form which is often more convenient for calculations. This can be done by considering typical terms of the equation. Thus, as $\mathbf{I}$ and $\mathbf{J}$ commute with each other,

$$\sum_{ij}(\mathbf{I})_i(\mathbf{I})_j(\mathbf{J})_i(\mathbf{J})_j = \left\{\sum_i (\mathbf{I})_i(\mathbf{J})_i\right\}\left\{\sum_j (\mathbf{I})_j(\mathbf{J})_j\right\} = (\mathbf{I}\cdot\mathbf{J})^2$$

Likewise

$$\sum_{ij}(\mathbf{I})_i(\mathbf{I})_j\,\delta_{ij}\mathbf{J}^2 = \left[\sum_i (\mathbf{I})_i^2\right]\mathbf{J}^2 = \mathbf{I}^2\mathbf{J}^2$$

and

$$\sum_{ij}\delta_{ij}\mathbf{I}^2\mathbf{J}^2 = 3\mathbf{I}^2\mathbf{J}^2$$

The only complicated terms are

$$\sum_{ij}(\mathbf{I})_j(\mathbf{I})_i(\mathbf{J})_i(\mathbf{J})_j = \sum_{ij}(\mathbf{I})_i(\mathbf{I})_j(\mathbf{J})_j(\mathbf{J})_i$$

In this, from the usual commutation rules (C16) for angular momentum operators, we can write

$$(\mathbf{I})_i(\mathbf{I})_j = (\mathbf{I})_j(\mathbf{I})_i + i(\mathbf{I})_{i\times j}$$

where the subscript $i \times j$ indicates the component perpendicular to the i and j components as in a vector product. Therefore

$$\sum_{ij}(\mathbf{I})_i(\mathbf{I})_j(\mathbf{J})_j(\mathbf{J})_i = \sum_{ij}(\mathbf{I})_j(\mathbf{I})_i(\mathbf{J})_j(\mathbf{J})_i + i\sum_{ij}(\mathbf{I})_{i\times j}(\mathbf{J})_j(\mathbf{J})_i$$

$$= (\mathbf{I}\cdot\mathbf{J})^2 + i\sum_{ij}(\mathbf{I})_{i\times j}(\mathbf{J})_j(\mathbf{J})_i$$

But

$$(\mathbf{J})_j(\mathbf{J})_i = \frac{(\mathbf{J})_j(\mathbf{J})_i + (\mathbf{J})_j(\mathbf{J})_i}{2} = \frac{(\mathbf{J})_j(\mathbf{J})_i + (\mathbf{J})_i(\mathbf{J})_j + i(\mathbf{J})_{j\times i}}{2}$$

so

$$i\sum_{ij}(\mathbf{I})_{i\times j}(\mathbf{J})_j(\mathbf{J})_i = \frac{i}{2}\sum_{ij}(\mathbf{I})_{i\times j}[(\mathbf{J})_j(\mathbf{J})_i + (\mathbf{J})_i(\mathbf{J})_j] - \frac{1}{2}\sum_{ij}(\mathbf{I})_{i\times j}(\mathbf{J})_{j\times i}$$

However, the terms of the first sum on the right are antisymmetric in i and j and the sum vanishes. Therefore

$$i \sum_{ij} (\mathbf{I})_{i \times j}(\mathbf{J})_j \cdot (\mathbf{J})_i = -\tfrac{1}{2} \sum_{ij} (\mathbf{I})_{i \times j}(\mathbf{J})_{j \times i} = \tfrac{1}{2} \sum_{ij} (\mathbf{I})_{i \times j}(\mathbf{J})_{i \times j}$$

$$= \tfrac{1}{2} \sum_k 2(\mathbf{I})_k (\mathbf{J})_k = \mathbf{I} \cdot \mathbf{J}$$

Therefore

$$\Sigma(\mathbf{I})_i(\mathbf{I})_j(\mathbf{J})_j(\mathbf{J})_i = (\mathbf{I} \cdot \mathbf{J})^2 + \mathbf{I} \cdot \mathbf{J}$$

and

$$\mathfrak{H}_Q = \frac{1}{6} \frac{e^2 q_J Q}{I(2I-1)J(2J-1)} \left\{ \frac{9}{2} (\mathbf{I} \cdot \mathbf{J})^2 + \frac{9}{2}[(\mathbf{I} \cdot \mathbf{J})^2 + (\mathbf{I} \cdot \mathbf{J})] \right.$$

$$\left. - 3\mathbf{I}^2\mathbf{J}^2 - 3\mathbf{I}^2\mathbf{J}^2 + 3\mathbf{I}^2\mathbf{J}^2 \right\}$$

$$= \frac{e^2 q_J Q}{2I(2I-1)J(2J-1)} \left[3(\mathbf{I} \cdot \mathbf{J})^2 + \frac{3}{2}\mathbf{I} \cdot \mathbf{J} - \mathbf{I}^2\mathbf{J}^2 \right] \qquad (48)$$

which is the form of the quadrupole interaction used above.

Although Eq. (48) is the one conventionally used for discussing quadrupole interactions in atoms, it is less convenient for quadrupole moments of $^1\Sigma$ linear molecules rotating with different rotational angular momentum quantum numbers J. This is true because the quantity q_J is dependent on the magnitude of J. Hence it is desirable in the molecular case to replace q_J by a quantity which is expressed in terms of the molecule's axis instead of an axis fixed in space, since such a quantity will be the same for molecules which differ only in m_J and J.

For this transformation let z_0 be along the axis of symmetry of the molecule and let θ_e and ϕ_e be the angular spherical polar coordinates of a point in the molecule relative to an external z axis while θ_e' and ϕ_e' are the coordinates relative to the molecular axis of symmetry z_0. Also let θ'' and ϕ'' be the angles expressing the position of the z_0 axis relative to the z axis. Then, by the spherical harmonic addition theorem as summarized by Condon and Shortley (C16, p. 54),

$$3 \cos^2 \theta_e - 1 = \tfrac{1}{2}(3 \cos^2 \theta'' - 1)(3 \cos^2 \theta_e' - 1) + \text{terms involving } e^{i\phi''}$$

$$(49)$$

Now, however, by Condon and Shortley (C16, p. 51), the wave function for a rotating molecule in the rotational state $m_J = J$ is

$$\psi_{JJ}(\theta'', \phi'') = \frac{(-1)^J}{\sqrt{2\pi}} \sqrt{\frac{(2J+1)!}{2}} \frac{1}{2^J J!} \sin^J \theta'' e^{iJ\phi''} \qquad (50)$$

Therefore, the average of Eq. (49) over the rotational state can be found by multiplying Eq. (49) by $|\psi_{JJ}|^2$ and integrating over all angles with $d\Omega = \sin\theta\, d\theta\, d\phi$. From this and the use of Peirce's integral 483 (P8) the following is obtained immediately:

$$<3\cos^2\theta_e - 1>_{m_J=J} = -\frac{J}{2J+3}(3\cos^2\theta_e' - 1)$$

Therefore

$$q_J = \frac{1}{e}\int \frac{3z_e^2 - r_e^2}{r^5}\rho^e_{e,m_J=J}\, d\tau$$

$$= \frac{1}{e}\int \frac{3\cos^2\theta_e - 1}{r_e^3}\rho^e_{e,m_J=J}\, d\tau$$

$$= -\frac{J}{2J+3}\frac{1}{e}\int \frac{3\cos^2\theta_e' - 1}{r_e^3}\rho^e\, d\tau'$$

$$= -\frac{J}{2J+3}\frac{1}{e}\frac{\partial^2 V^e}{\partial z_0^2} \tag{51}$$

where

$$\frac{\partial^2 V^e}{\partial z_0^2} = \int \frac{3\cos^2\theta_e' - 1}{r_e^5}\rho^e\, d\tau' \tag{52}$$

As is apparent from the form of this expression, V^e can be interpreted as the potential from all charges external to a small sphere surrounding the nucleus.

It is important to emphasize that V^e is not the potential V of all electrical charges from the rest of the molecule, including the electron density of the molecule inside the nuclear radius. The difference between these two can readily be evaluated. Let ρ_1 be the electronic charge density at the nucleus, and assume that in the immediate vicinity of the nucleus it is spherically symmetric. Then, as $V - V^e$ arises solely from the spherically symmetric charge distribution ρ_1, from Poisson's equation

$$\frac{\partial^2(V-V^e)}{\partial x^2} + \frac{\partial^2(V-V^e)}{\partial y^2} + \frac{\partial^2(V-V^e)}{\partial z^2} = 4\pi\rho_1 = 3\frac{\partial^2(V-V^e)}{\partial z^2} \tag{53}$$

so

$$\frac{\partial^2 V}{\partial z^2} = \frac{\partial^2 V^e}{\partial z^2} + \frac{4\pi}{3}\rho_1 \tag{54}$$

Owing to its spherical symmetry the ρ_1 term does not affect the nuclear quadrupole interaction.

From Eqs. (48) and (52) it follows immediately that

$$\mathfrak{H}_Q = -\frac{eQ(\partial^2 V^e/\partial z_0{}^2)}{2I(2I-1)(2J+3)(2J-1)}\left[3(\mathbf{I}\cdot\mathbf{J})^2 + \frac{3}{2}\mathbf{I}\cdot\mathbf{J} - \mathbf{I}^2\mathbf{J}^2\right]$$
(55)

If the molecule instead of being a linear molecule is a symmetric top, the above can easily be extended to include this case. For a symmetric-top molecule the angular momentum is no longer exactly perpendicular to the molecular axis; therefore, to define the situation, an extra quantity $(\mathbf{J})_{z_0}$ must be introduced which measures the component of J along the axis of the molecule so that, if θ''' is the angle between J and the internuclear axis,

$$\cos\theta''' = \frac{(\mathbf{J})_{z_0}}{|\mathbf{J}|}$$
(56)

For a symmetric-top molecule a procedure analogous to that for Eq. (49) therefore directly yields the relation

$$\mathfrak{H}_Q = -\frac{eQ(\partial^2 V^e/\partial z_0{}^2)}{2I(2I-1)(2J+3)(2J-1)}\left[1 - \frac{3(\mathbf{J})_{z_0}{}^2}{\mathbf{J}^2}\right]$$
$$\times [3(\mathbf{I}\cdot\mathbf{J})^2 + \tfrac{3}{2}\mathbf{I}\cdot\mathbf{J} - \mathbf{I}^2\mathbf{J}^2]$$
(57)

Addendum. The theorem used in the derivation of Eq. (42) is most easily proved by group theory methods (W10, W14). However, it may be derived in a less subtle though more tedious fashion from the matrix elements of a vector and the laws of matrix multiplication. Let $\mathbf{T}$ be any vector associated with the nucleus and satisfying the same commutation rules with respect to $\mathbf{I}$ as $\mathbf{r}$ or $\mathbf{I}$. Let α represent all the quantum numbers except I and m_I that are associated with the nucleus in an I, m_I representation, and let m temporarily be written for m_I. Then the matrix elements that are desired are

$$\left(\alpha I m\left|3\frac{T_iT_j + T_jT_i}{2} - \delta_{ij}T^2\right|\alpha I m'\right)$$
(58)

However, the matrix of a product equals the product of the matrices; thus, for example,

$$(\alpha I m|\,T_iT_j\,|\alpha I m') = \sum_{\alpha''I''m''} (\alpha I m|\,T_i\,|\alpha''I''m'')(\alpha''I''m''|\,T_j\,|\alpha I m')$$
(59)

Hence the desired matrix can be calculated from the matrices of the components of the corresponding vector $\mathbf{T}$. Note, however, that, although only matrix elements of T_iT_j diagonal in I are desired, they depend on matrix elements of T_i that are non-diagonal in I. It is this dependence on non-diagonal elements of the vector that makes the proof lengthy instead of trivial.

The well-known matrix elements (C16, P5) for a vector are

$$(\alpha Im|\; \mathbf{T}\; |\alpha'I + 1m \pm 1) = \mp T_{\alpha I;\, \alpha'I+1\frac{1}{2}} \sqrt{(I\pm m+1)(I\pm m+2)}(\mathbf{i}\pm i\mathbf{j})$$

$$(\alpha Im|\; \mathbf{T}\; |\alpha'I + 1m) = T_{\alpha I;\, \alpha'I+1}\sqrt{(I + 1)^2 - m^2}\,\mathbf{k}$$

$$(\alpha Im|\; \mathbf{T}\; |\alpha'Im \pm 1) = T_{\alpha I;\, \alpha'I\frac{1}{2}}\sqrt{(I \mp m)(I \pm m + 1)}(\mathbf{i} \pm i\mathbf{j}) \quad (60)$$

$$(\alpha Im|\; \mathbf{T}\; |\alpha'Im) = T_{\alpha I;\, \alpha'I}m\,\mathbf{k}$$

$$(\alpha Im|\; \mathbf{T}\; |\alpha'I - 1m \pm 1) = \pm T_{\alpha I;\, \alpha'I-1\frac{1}{2}}\sqrt{(I \mp m)(I \mp m - 1)}(\mathbf{i} \pm i\mathbf{j})$$

$$(\alpha Im|\; \mathbf{T}\; |\alpha'I - 1m) = T_{\alpha I;\, \alpha'I-1}\sqrt{I^2 - m^2}\,\mathbf{k}$$

From Eqs. (59) and (60) the matrix elements of Eq. (58) can be directly calculated. These expressions can be simplified by the use of various algebraic identities such as

$$\sqrt{(I \pm m + 1)(I \pm m + 2)([j + 1]^2 - [m \pm 1]^2)}$$
$$= (I \pm m + 2)\sqrt{(I \pm m + 1)(I \mp m)}$$

The matrix elements of Eq. (58) then directly become

$$\left(\alpha Im \left| 3\frac{T_iT_j + T_jT_i}{2} - \delta_{ij}\mathbf{T}^2 \right| \alpha Im'\right)$$

$$= \left\{\sum_{\alpha'} [-\tfrac{3}{2}T_{\alpha I;\, \alpha'I+1}T_{\alpha'I+1;\, \alpha I} - \tfrac{3}{2}T_{\alpha I;\, \alpha'I-1}T_{\alpha'I-1;\, \alpha I}\right.$$
$$\left. + \tfrac{3}{2}T_{\alpha I;\, \alpha'I}T_{\alpha'I;\, \alpha I}]\right\} \cdot \{[\sqrt{(I \mp m)(I \mp m - 1)(I \pm m + 1)(I \pm m + 2)}]$$

$$\times \tfrac{1}{2}[\delta_{i1}\,\delta_{j1} - \delta_{i2}\,\delta_{j2} \pm i(\delta_{i1}\,\delta_{j2} + \delta_{i2}\,\delta_{j1})]\,\delta_{m'm\pm2}$$

$$+ [(2m \pm 1)\sqrt{(I \mp m)(I \pm m + 1)}\,]\tfrac{1}{2}[\delta_{i3}\,\delta_{j1} + \delta_{i1}\,\delta_{j3}$$

$$\pm i(\delta_{i3}\,\delta_{j2} + \delta_{i2}\,\delta_{j3})]\delta_{m'm\pm1} + \sqrt{\tfrac{2}{3}}[3m^2 - I(I + 1)]$$

$$\times \sqrt{\tfrac{2}{3}}[\delta_{i3}\,\delta_{j3} - \tfrac{1}{2}\delta_{i1}\,\delta_{j1} - \delta_{i2}\tfrac{1}{2}\delta_{j2}]\delta_{m'm}\} \quad (61)$$

Since all the constants $T_{\alpha I;\, \alpha'I'}$ combine in the above to make a common factor with all the m dependence being contained in the other factor, the m dependence of the above tensor components are the same for all such tensors regardless of the different relative values of the constants $T_{\alpha I; \alpha' I'}$ possessed by different vectors $\mathbf{T}$. This then gives the desired theorem. Equation (61) also provides the m dependence of the matrix elements, and this is of value in the analysis of any problem in detail.

D. Appendix B. Theoretical Restrictions on the Orders of Electrical Multipoles

1. Parity Restrictions. From parity considerations it will first be shown that, if all nuclear electrical effects arise from electrical charges and if the nuclear Hamiltonian is unaltered by an inversion of the coordinate system, no odd (l odd) nuclear electrical multipole moment can exist.

For the proof of this, consider the parity operator R which inverts the space coordinates, i.e., reverses the signs of the components of a vector $\mathbf{r}_n$. If $\mathfrak{H}$ is the Hamiltonian of the nuclear system, by assumption $\mathfrak{H}$ and R commute, whence if there is no degeneracy the eigenfunctions of $\mathfrak{H}$ are also eigenfunctions of R. Hence, if R' is the eigenvalue of the operator R and if $\psi(\mathbf{r})$ is a non-degenerate eigenfunction of $\mathfrak{H}$,

$$R\psi(x_n, y_n, z_n) = R'\psi(x_n, y_n, z_n) = \psi(-x_n, -y_n, -z_n) \qquad (62)$$

Then

$$R^2\psi(x_n, y_n, z_n) = R\psi(-x_n, -y_n, -z_n)$$

$$= \psi(x_n, y_n, z_n) = R'^2\psi(x_n, y_n, z_n) \qquad (63)$$

Hence

$$R'^2 = 1 \qquad (64)$$

or

$$R' = \pm 1 \qquad (65)$$

Therefore, with the above assumptions, all states must be of either even or odd parity, i.e., must have eigenfunctions that are multiplied by either $+1$ or -1 on inversion of coordinates. In either case $\psi^*\psi$ is unaltered on inversion of coordinates; therefore

$$\rho_n(x_n, y_n, z_n) = \rho_n(-x_n, -y_n, -z_n) \qquad (66)$$

However, from Eqs. (5) and (6) it is apparent that, in so far as the nuclear coordinates are concerned, the multipole of order 2 is proportional to

$$\int_{\tau_n} r_n{}^l \rho_n(x_n, y_n, z_n) P_l \, d\tau_n \qquad (67)$$

An inversion of coordinates in polar coordinates corresponds to $\theta \rightarrow \pi - \theta$, $\phi \rightarrow \pi + \phi$, and $r \rightarrow r$, so P_l has its sign changed on inversion if l is odd and is unaltered if l is even; therefore

$$P_l(-x_n, -y_n, -z_n) = (-1)^l P_l(x_n, y_n, z_n) \qquad (68)$$

Therefore, from Eqs. (66) and (67), if l is odd, the contribution from $-x_n, -y_n, -z_n$ in the integral (67) just cancels the contribution from x_n, y_n, z_n. Therefore the integral vanishes and no odd electrical multipole moment can be observed.

2. Upper Limit to Electrical Multipole Order. It can next be shown that for a nuclear spin I it is impossible to observe a nuclear electrical multipole moment of order 2^l greater than that corresponding to $l = 2I$, where I is the nuclear spin.

For the proof of this, consider the 2^l multipole interaction term which, from Eq. (67), can be written as proportional to

$$\int_{\tau_n} r_n{}^l \psi_n{}^* P_l \psi_n \, d\tau_n \qquad (69)$$

However, by the assumption that the nuclear spin is I, ψ_n and $\psi_n{}^*$ are each eigenfunctions corresponding to an angular momentum I. Since $r_n{}^l$ has no angular dependence, $r_n{}^l \psi_n{}^*$ is also an eigenfunction of angular momentum I. However, as is well known (C16), P_l is also an eigenfunction of an angular momentum and corresponds to angular momentum l. Therefore the product of P_l and ψ_n corresponds to a wave function in which the angular moments I and l are combined. By the vector model for combining angular momentum,[1] $P_l \psi_n$ will therefore correspond to an angular momentum between $l + I$ and $|l - I|$. However, in the integral (69), $r_n{}^l \psi_n{}^*$ and $P_l \psi_n$ will be orthogonal and the integral will vanish unless they correspond to eigenfunctions with the same angular momentum eigenvalues. Therefore, in order that Eq. (69) may not vanish, I must lie between $l + I$ and $|l - I|$. As this can occur only if $l \leq 2I$, the above statement is proved.

E. Appendix C. Magnetic Hyperfine Structure Constants

What is desired is a calculation of the constant a in Eq. (21). By Eq. (22) this can be obtained if the magnetic field $\mathbf{H}_J$ arising from the electrons can be evaluated at the nucleus. For a hydrogen-like atom, $\mathbf{H}_J$ can be calculated from the following simple classical considerations

---

[1] For a detailed justification of this use of the vector model see Condon and Shortley (C16, pp. 57, 58).

illustrated in Fig. 5. The electron's magnetic field arises from the combination of the field $\mathbf{H}_L$, due to the electron's orbital motion, and the field $\mathbf{H}_S$, due to the electron's spin magnetic moment; therefore

$$\mathbf{H}_J = \mathbf{H}_L + \mathbf{H}_S \tag{70}$$

But, classically, if $\mathbf{v}$ is the electron's velocity, $\mathbf{r}$ the position of the elec-

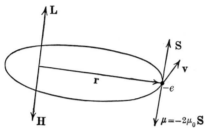

Fig. 5. Schematic diagram of the interaction of the nucleus with the orbital and spin magnetic fields of the electron in an atom.

tron relative to the nucleus, and $\mathbf{L}$ the electron's orbital angular momentum in units of $\hbar$

$$\mathbf{H}_L = \frac{-e\mathbf{v} \times (-\mathbf{r})}{cr^3} = \frac{-\mathbf{r} \times m\mathbf{v}}{r^3} \frac{e}{mc} = -2\mu_0 \frac{\mathbf{L}}{r^3} \tag{71}$$

where μ_0 is the Bohr magneton $e\hbar/2mc$. Likewise, from expressions for the field of a classical magnetic dipole, $\boldsymbol{\mu} = -2\mu_0\mathbf{S}$,

$$\mathbf{H}_S = -\frac{1}{r^3}\left[\boldsymbol{\mu} - \frac{3(\boldsymbol{\mu}\cdot\mathbf{r})\mathbf{r}}{r^2}\right] = \frac{2\mu_0}{r^3}\left[\mathbf{S} - \frac{3(\mathbf{S}\cdot\mathbf{r})\mathbf{r}}{r^2}\right] \tag{72}$$

Then

$$\mathbf{H}_J \cdot \mathbf{J} = (\mathbf{H}_L + \mathbf{H}_S)\cdot\mathbf{J} = -\frac{2\mu_0}{r^3}\left[\mathbf{L} - \mathbf{S} + 3\left(\mathbf{S}\cdot\frac{\mathbf{r}}{r}\right)\frac{\mathbf{r}}{r}\right]\cdot(\mathbf{L} + \mathbf{S}) \tag{73}$$

Only the value of this expression averaged over the electron's motion is of interest, so that, after the scalar multiplication is made, the terms may be averaged over the electron's motion. Terms with a factor $\mathbf{L}\cdot\mathbf{r}/r$ may be omitted since they equal zero. Then, if $<1/r^3>$ indicates the averaged value of $1/r^3$, the average value of $\mathbf{H}_J \cdot \mathbf{J}$ is

$$\mathbf{H}_J \cdot \mathbf{J} = (\mathbf{H}_L + \mathbf{H}_S)\cdot\mathbf{J} = -2\mu_0 < \frac{1}{r^3} > \left[L(L+1) - S(S+1)\right.$$
$$\left. + 3\left(\mathbf{S}\cdot\frac{\mathbf{r}}{r}\right)^2\right] \tag{74}$$

But $\mathbf{S} \cdot \mathbf{r}/r$ is just the component of $\mathbf{S}$ in the direction $\mathbf{r}/r$. Therefore for an electron with spin $\frac{1}{2}$ it is $\pm \frac{1}{2}$, so that the square of this quantity is necessarily $+\frac{1}{4}$. With this and $S = \frac{1}{2}$, Eq. (74) becomes

$$\mathbf{H}_J \cdot \mathbf{J} = -2\mu_0 < \frac{1}{r^3} > L(L + 1) \qquad (75)$$

For hydrogen-like atoms, $<1/r^3>$ is well known [1] and is

$$< \frac{1}{r^3} > = \frac{Z^3}{a_0^3 n^3 (L + 1)(L + \frac{1}{2})L} \qquad (76)$$

where a_0 is the radius of the first Bohr orbit of a hydrogen atom or $\hbar^2/me^2$. Therefore, from Eq. (22),

$$a = \frac{2\mu_0(\mu_I/I)Z^3}{a_0^3 n^3 (L + \frac{1}{2})J(J + 1)} = \frac{2\pi\hbar c \, \mathrm{Ry} \, \alpha^2 Z^3 g_I}{n^3 (L + \frac{1}{2})J(J + 1)(M/m)} \qquad (77)$$

where the last form is expressed in terms of the Rydberg constant $\mathrm{Ry} = me^4/4\pi\hbar^3 c$ and the fine structure constant $\alpha = e^2/\hbar c$. This equation is the result used in Eq. (25). It should be noted that this discussion is not rigorous when applied to an S state, since then Eq. (76) becomes infinite and Eq. (75) indeterminate. Nevertheless, if in Eq. (77) the values $L = 0$ and $J = \frac{1}{2}$ are substituted, the result is

$$a = \frac{8}{3} \frac{2\pi\hbar c \, \mathrm{Ry} \, \alpha^2 Z^3 g_I}{n^3 (M/m)} \qquad (78)$$

which is just the result of Eq. (24) that has been calculated in a rigorous relativistic wave-mechanical manner by Fermi (F8) and others.

[1] See, for example, Condon and Shortley (C16, p. 117).

3

EXPERIMENTAL METHODS OF MEASURING NUCLEAR MOMENTS AND STATISTICS

A. Hyperfine Structure in Optical Atomic Spectra

The experimental techniques for the optical study of hyperfine structure are those of ordinary optical spectroscopy. However, because of the very close spacing ($\Delta\nu \sim 0.05$ cm^{-1}) of many hyperfine structure lines, highly refined techniques must commonly be used. Carefully made Fabry-Perot etalons are often used to resolve the lines. Special light sources have been developed by Schüler and others which can be well cooled to reduce Doppler broadening and which are designed to reduce absorption broadening; use is often made of hollow cathode discharges in which the cathode is a hollow cylinder, as illustrated in Fig. 6, which can be well cooled, often with liquid air. Jackson and Kuhn (J5), Minkowski (M23), Meissner (M14), Paul (P3), and others have designed their light sources so the emitting atoms are in a directed atomic beam which can be viewed transversely to reduce Doppler effect, as in Fig. 7. Fuller descriptions and summaries of the optical techniques employed and of the detailed methods of term analysis have been given by Tolansky (T11) and by Kopfermann (K29).

The spin can be determined from hyperfine structure studies in several different ways. The easiest way, when applicable, is merely to use the number of components of the spectral line. If the hyperfine structure of one of the set of states concerned in the transition is negligibly small compared to the other, the number of hyperfine structure lines will be either $2J + 1$ or $2I + 1$ according as $I > J$ or $J > I$. Consequently, if J is sufficiently large, I can be obtained merely by counting the number of lines. Even if the hyperfine structure of one state is not negligibly small, this procedure can be used if a term analysis of the spectrum is possible, in which case all that is necessary is to determine the multiplicity of a term for which $J > I$.

Even if measurements cannot be made on a state for which $J > I$, the spin can sometimes be determined by measuring the relative spacing of the components of a term and using the interval rule, Eqs. (23) and (29), to determine the different F values and consequently to determine I. However, great care must be exercised in using this method to make

27

sure that there are no misleading departures from the interval rule due
either to perturbations of neighboring states as discussed in Section 2
or to an electrical quadrupole moment.

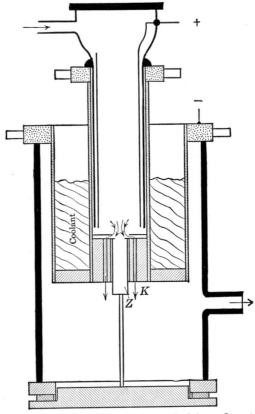

Fig. 6.   Hollow cathode discharge source for optical hyperfine structure studies.
The light is observed through the glass plate at the top, the thallium being studied
is placed in the hollow aluminum cylinder Z, and the discharge is maintained with
0.7 mm pressure of argon (K31).

The relative intensities of the components of a hyperfine structure
multiplet can be correlated (T11, K29) with the F values of the states
concerned, and consequently, if J is known for the states, I can be
inferred.   Thus, if only one of the observed terms is split, the intensities
of the hyperfine structure components are proportional to the statistical
weights of the split terms, i.e., proportional to $2F + 1$.   From the relative intensities, then, the maximum value of F can be inferred, and,
from this and the known J, I is determined.   This method is useful

when the spin cannot be determined from the number of components, but it is much less reliable.

A quite reliable but often difficult method of obtaining the nuclear spin is to apply a strong external magnetic field and observe the multiplicity of the lines in the Paschen-Back effect. In this limit Eq. (35) applies with the first term being the biggest one, with the second term

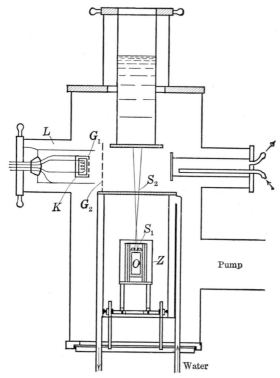

Fig. 7. Typical atomic beam source for optical hyperfine structure measurements. The beam emerges from the oven O and is cross-bombarded by the electron beam from cathode K(P3).

being negligible owing to the smallness of μ_{NM}, and with the multiplicity being determined by the last term. Since m_I can have $2I + 1$ different values, the multiplicity of the state for a given m_J will be $2I + 1$. Since in the strong field case $\Delta m_I = 0$, each transition $m_J \rightarrow m_J'$ will therefore consist of $2I + 1$ components.

The sign of the magnetic moment can often be obtained directly from the hyperfine structure, particularly for alkali-like spectra where the signs of the factors entering into the determination of the constant a

in Eq. (22) are known. The sign of the moment is determined by whether the term order is normal, i.e., if the hfs term with the largest F lies above, or inverted, with the largest F lying below. The normal order corresponds to a positive moment and the inverted to a negative moment. The term order is usually experimentally determined from a comparison of the intensity of the components.

The magnitude of the nuclear magnetic moments is obtained from the hyperfine structure by making a term analysis of the observed spectrum from which the quantity a of Eqs. (22) and (23) can be obtained, and, from this value together with Eqs. (24) and (25) or the alternative formulas of Section 2, the value of μ_I may be obtained. This value of μ_I is usually only approximate since the relation between a and μ_I is only approximate. Schüler, Tolansky, Kopfermann, and others have measured a number of magnetic moments in this way. The results, together with references to the original papers, are given in Section 4.

In interpreting the hyperfine spectrum of elements care must be taken (K29) to avoid confusion of the nuclear hyperfine structure with the isotope shift, since this shift is often of a magnitude comparable to the nuclear hyperfine structure. The isotope shift is of two kinds: (1) a pure mass effect corresponding to the fact that the nucleus with its non-infinite mass is not a motionless attracting center to the electrons, and (2) the volume and polarizability effects discussed on page 8. The first of these is most important for light elements such as hydrogen and lithium, and the second is the important cause of isotope shift in heavy atoms. However, it should be noted that for atoms with more than one electron the mass dependent isotope shift is more complicated than a mere reduced mass calculation. The magnitude of the shift depends on the way that the electrons are coupled together in their motion. Thus, if two electrons are always on opposite sides of the nucleus, the mass effect is much less than if they are always on the same side. The exchange coupling between electrons provides a mechanism for relating their phases. A calculation of the isotope shift to be expected for Li II has been made by Hughes and Eckart (H16a).

Even when the hyperfine spectrum cannot be resolved, it is sometimes possible to estimate the interaction constant a and consequently the nuclear gyromagnetic ratio from a study of the polarization of resonance radiation, with incident polarized light, as a function of the strength of an externally applied magnetic field. The extent of the polarization of the resonance radiation is a function of H/a, and consequently the constant a can be obtained from the measurement. Hyperfine separations less than 10^{-3} cm^{-1} have been studied in this way.

The method has been used by Ellet and Heydenburg (E1) to study the small separations of sodium and cesium.

As discussed in Section 2B, departures from the interval rule, Eqs. (23) and (29), can occur for two reasons: (1) magnetic perturbations of nearby energy levels and (2) effects of a nuclear electrical quadrupole moment. The spectrum of mercurous iodide is a good example (S16) of a departure of the first type. However, Schüler and Schmidt (S24) found in europium departures from the interval rule which could not be attributed to magnetic perturbations and which had all the characteristics of a nuclear electrical quadrupole interaction as discussed in Section 2A, including the possibility of accounting for the term energies by a combination of Eqs. (8) and (20), i.e., by the assumption of both a magnetic dipole and a nuclear electrical quadrupole interaction. Since this first measurement, a number of similar departures from the interval rule have been found with the result that from the magnitude of the departure and from the methods of estimating q discussed in Section 2A, a number of nuclear electrical quadrupole moments have been determined from hyperfine structure measurements. These results are tabulated in Section 4C.

B. Band Spectra Measurements

An important means of measuring nuclear spins has been to study the band spectra of homonuclear diatomic molecules, i.e., diatomic molecules whose two nuclei are identical, such as H_2. This measurement is possible because of the symmetry restrictions on the allowed complete wave functions of diatomic molecules with identical nuclei, i.e., the complete wave function must be symmetrical in the nuclear coordinates for nuclei of even mass number which, as discussed in Section 1A, satisfy Bose-Einstein statistics, and the wave function is antisymmetrical for odd mass number or Fermi-Dirac statistics.

A gas of homonuclear diatomic molecules essentially consists of molecules of two types: (1) molecules whose combined nuclear spin wave functions are symmetric in the two nuclei or so-called ortho molecules, and (2) para molecules whose nuclear spin wave functions are anti-symmetric. There is little intercombination between these two, since a transition from one type to the other can be induced only by a collision which acts quite differently on the spin of one nucleus than on the other so as to induce a relative reorientation. For given electronic and vibrational states, one of the above types of molecules can exist only in even rotation states (which are symmetrical in the nuclear coordinates), and the other type can exist only in odd rotational states since the total wave function must be such as to satisfy the symmetry requirement of the preceding paragraph. Whether the ortho molecule has odd rotational quantum number J and the para molecule even J or whether it is *vice versa* is determined by a combination of the symmetry in the nuclei of the electron states and the statistics satisfied by the nucleus, since the requirement is merely that the total wave function have the proper symmetry in the nuclear coordinates.

The statistical weights of the ortho and para molecules and, consequently, the relative abundances are different. If the nuclear spin is I, there are $2I + 1$ different spin wave functions for a single nucleus, e.g., $\chi_1, \chi_2, \cdots, \chi_{2I+1}$, corresponding to the $2I + 1$ different allowed values of m_I. For molecules of two identical nuclei the number of anti-symmetric spin wave functions such as $\frac{1}{2}[\chi_1(1)\chi_3(2) - \chi_1(2)\chi_3(1)]$ is equal to the number of ways $2I + 1$ wave functions can be combined two at a time or $(2I + 1)!/2!(2I - 1)! = I(2I + 1)$, which is therefore the number of para spin states. Corresponding to each of the above anti-symmetric spin wave functions a symmetric spin wave function can be formed by replacing the minus sign with a plus. In addition, however, the $2I + 1$ states $\chi_1(1)\chi_1(2), \cdots, \chi_{2I+1}(1)\chi_{2I+1}(2)$ are also symmetric, so that the number of ortho spin states is $I(2I + 1) + (2I + 1) = (I + 1)(2I + 1)$. Therefore the relative weight (and consequently relative abundance) of the ortho and para molecules is

$$\frac{n_0}{n_p} = \frac{I + 1}{I} \tag{79}$$

Consequently, alternate rotational energy states of the molecule will be populated in this ratio, and the intensities of alternate band spectra and Raman effect lines will be in the above ratio; therefore measurement of these intensities gives a direct determination of the spin. This method is particularly effective for low values of spin, since the above ratio departs markedly from unity for low values of I. Thus $(I + 1)/I$ for $I = 0$ is ∞ (alternate lines are missing), for $I = \frac{1}{2}$ is 3, for $I = 1$ is 2, for $I = \frac{3}{2}$ is $\frac{5}{3}$, etc.

When the symmetry in the nuclei of the electron wave function is known, an experimental evaluation of whether it is the states of even or odd J that are most abundant determines whether the nucleus follows Fermi-Dirac or Bose-Einstein statistics. The statistics of a number of nuclei have been determined in this way. All results obtained so far are in agreement with the general rule that nuclei of even mass number obey Bose-Einstein statistics and those of odd mass number obey Fermi-Dirac statistics. Figure 8 shows a typical band spectrum with alternating intensities of spectral lines.

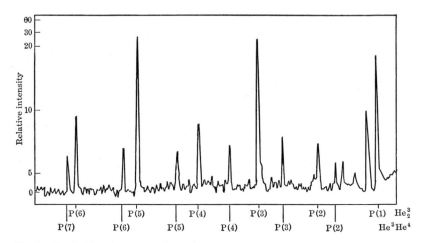

Fig. 8.   Typical band spectrum in nuclear spin measurements.   This is a photometer curve of a portion of the P branch of $He_2{}^3$ and He^3He^4.   The calibrated relative intensity is as marked on the ordinate.   The alternate intensities of the $He_2{}^3$ lines are in the ratio 2.8 to 1, which is close to the theoretical ratio of 3 to 1 appropriate to spin $\frac{1}{2}$ and far from a ratio of 1.67 which would be appropriate for a spin of $\frac{3}{2}$ (D15).

C. Molecular and Atomic Beam Non-Resonance Methods

1. Molecular Beam Deflection Experiments.   By essentially a highly refined form of the Stern-Gerlach experiment, Frisch and Stern (F21) and Estermann, Stern, and Simpson (E3, E4) in a series of experiments measured the magnetic moments of the proton and deuteron by the deflection of the diatomic hydrogen molecules of a collimated beam which passes through an inhomogeneous magnetic deflecting field. These experiments with magnetic moments of nuclear magneton instead of Bohr magneton magnitude are necessarily difficult.   Much longer deflecting paths and large field gradients are needed.   Although the electronic state of the hydrogen molecule is $^1\Sigma$ so that the non-rotating molecule has no electron magnetic moment, there is a magnetic moment induced by the rotation of the molecule which is of a magnitude comparable to the nuclear moments.   Hence the deflection of the beam due to the rotational magnetic moment must be allowed for.   This was done in these experiments by making measurements with pure parahydrogen, for which the nuclear spins are opposed and consequently produce no deflection.   Since all the deflection in the parahydrogen experiment was therefore due to the rotational magnetic moment, the experiment provided an empirical value for the rotational magnetic moment.   This value was then used as a correction in the experiments with ordinary hydrogen and deuterium.

2. Atomic Beam Deflection Method. Breit and Rabi (B35) first pointed out the possibility of measuring nuclear spins and magnetic moments by studying the deflection of beams of atoms which have finite electron moments and are consequently much more easily deflected in an inhomogeneous field. Data on nuclear spins and moments are obtainable from such studies since, as discussed in detail below, the magnitude of the nuclear moment determines the magnitude of the coupling between the nuclear spin and the electrons and consequently the strength of the externally applied magnetic field which is necessary to produce a given stage of intermediate coupling.

If the energy of an atom in magnetic field is W, the force upon such an atom in an inhomogeneous field is

$$F = -\frac{\partial W}{\partial z} = -\frac{\partial W}{\partial H}\frac{\partial H}{\partial z} \qquad (80)$$

Therefore the effective component of magnetic moment along z, the direction of the gradient, is

$$\mu_{\text{eff}} = -\frac{\partial W}{\partial H} \qquad (81)$$

However, in Eq. (36) we had an expression for the energy W as a function of magnetic field. The derivative of this with respect to H then gives μ_{eff}. This is plotted in Fig. 9 for $J = \frac{1}{2}$ and $I = \frac{1}{2}$ and $\frac{3}{2}$. The dashed lines correspond to the $F = I - \frac{1}{2}$ state provided that the nuclear magnetic moment is assumed positive (if it is negative this statement holds if the dashed lines are interchanged in position with the corresponding curved full lines and the straight lines are unaltered). It is easy to check that Fig. 9 is qualitatively of the right shape to be the derivative of Fig. 4.

These curves for μ_{eff} are dependent in both number and shape on the value of the nuclear spin. Consequently the nuclear spin can be determined from an analysis of the deflection pattern. Furthermore the abscissas of the above curves are

$$x = \frac{-\mu_J/J + \mu_I/I}{\Delta W}H \approx \frac{-(\mu_J/J)H}{\Delta W}$$

where ΔW is related to μ_I by Eqs. (37) and (22) just as in the hyperfine structure experiments. A measurement of the nature of the deflection pattern at a suitable intermediate field H therefore determines ΔW from which μ_I can be calculated. The spins and magnetic moments of hydrogen, deuterium, and sodium have been determined in this way by Rabi and his associates (R2, R3, R1).

3. Atomic Beam Zero Moment Method. A major evil of the atomic beam deflection method is that the amount of deflection suffered by an atom in passing through the inhomogeneous field is dependent on the velocity of the atom, which is in turn different for different atoms corre-

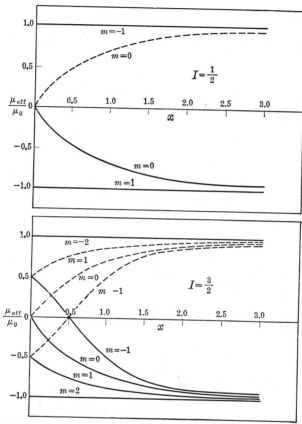

Fig. 9. Variation of moment with magnetic field. The dotted lines are the moments of the magnetic levels arising from $F = I - \frac{1}{2}$ state. Nuclear moment assumed positive (R4).

sponding to the thermal distribution of velocities in the beam. Consequently the deflection patterns instead of being sharp are considerably smeared and thus make accurate observations difficult. This difficulty was overcome by the so-called zero moment method. From the curves in Fig. 9 it can be seen that for a spin greater than $\frac{1}{2}$ there are one or more values of H for which $\mu_{eff} = 0$. For these values there will be no deflection, and this will be true for atoms of all velocities. The beam intensity as measured at the undeflected position will therefore rise through a large velocity independent maximum for these values of H. The positions of these maxima will also depend on H and not on the more difficultly measured $\partial H/\partial z$. From the numbers of such zero moment maxima and from their relative spacing (supplemented by deflection pattern measurements if $I \leq \frac{3}{2}$) the nuclear spin is determined. Likewise, from the fields required to produce the zero moment peak, ΔW and hence a can be obtained from which μ_I is calculated as in hyperfine structure experiments. This method has been applied by Rabi and his associates to a number of different atoms, notably atoms of alkalies, with sufficiently low ionization potentials that they can be detected with the so-called surface ionization detection (T2, F17, F18) technique. By a refinement of the method in the case of indium (M17) the interaction of the nuclear moment with the externally applied magnetic field was measured directly by virtue of the resolution being so high that the second term in Eq. (36) caused a measurable difference in the zero moment fields for the $F = I + \frac{1}{2}$ and $F = I - \frac{1}{2}$ states. Further refinements with indium and gallium (H5, R24) made possible the measurement of the nuclear electrical quadrupole moment which interacted with the metastable $^2P_{\frac{3}{2}}$ atomic states which were partially excited at the high oven temperature.

4. Atomic Beam Refocusing Methods. Unfortunately the zero moment method is not applicable for a spin of $\frac{1}{2}$ since from Fig. 9 the only zero moment in this case occurs for $H = 0$ at which there is no deflection even of a non-zero moment. The method is therefore not applicable to the important case of atomic hydrogen. Kellogg, Rabi, and Zacharias (R4, K7), however, devised a refocusing method which shared the zero moment method's advantage of being velocity independent although, unlike the zero moment method, a difficult measurement of $\partial H/\partial z$ was still required. In this experiment an initial deflection was produced with a weak magnetic field, so that μ_{eff}/μ_0 was approximately 0.5 for the inner states of Fig. 9. The beam was then allowed to pass into a second strong field region with inhomogeneity reversed. From Fig. 9 in this case $\mu_{\text{eff}} = \mu_0$ and is hence known. From the value of the gradient of the second field required exactly to compensate the deflection by the first field and from the gradient of the first field and the geometrical dimensions of the apparatus, the value of μ_{eff} in the first field could be calculated. From this and Fig. 9, x could be obtained and the value of H to produce this x in the first field could be measured. From these two values, μ_I could be calculated as in Section 3C3. This method was successfully applied to both the proton and the deuteron.

In this experiment the signs of the magnetic moments were also measured. From Fig. 9 the sign of the moment can be determined if it is possible to tell whether μ_{eff} of the state $F = I - \frac{1}{2}$ is positive or negative. The identification of which state has $F = I - \frac{1}{2} = 0$ can be made because the only m value for this state is zero, whereas for the $F = I + \frac{1}{2} = 1$ state the values $1, 0, -1$ are all possible. Consequently in the latter case non-adiabatic transitions between these states can take place in a region where H is low and rapidly changing in direction. This transition-inducing field is then placed between the deflecting and refocusing magnets of the hydrogen experiment, whose fields are set to refocus the middle states of Fig. 9. When the transition field is such as to induce transitions, the extent of the refocusing for the $F = I + \frac{1}{2}$ state is less because, by Fig. 9, one of the transitions can be to a state whose μ_{eff} is of opposite sign in the strong field limit. This does not happen, however, to the $F = I - \frac{1}{2}$ state. After the first deflecting field, a selector slit is introduced which can be moved to select atoms whose direction of deflection corresponds either to positive or negative μ_{eff}. A determination in this way of the sign of μ_{eff} for the state whose refocused intensity is unaffected by the presence or absence of the transition field therefore determines the sign of the nuclear moment. In this way the sign of the proton moment was determined as positive. A similar procedure may be applied to higher spins. In this way the signs of the moment of deuterium and a number of alkalies have been measured.

D. Molecular Beam Resonance Methods

The results by the above molecular beam non-resonance methods have almost all been superseded by the much more precise results obtainable with the molecular beam resonance method. In addition many moments which could not be measured at all by the former method have been measurable by the latter.

The resonance method developed by Rabi and his associates (R6, K9) provides a means for observing the reorientations of atomic, molecular, and nuclear moments relative to a constant homogeneous magnetic field when an oscillating or rotating magnetic field is superposed. The resonance reorientations, corresponding to absorption and stimulated emission, occur when the frequency of the oscillating field is in resonance with the frequency given by the Bohr relation:

$$2\pi\hbar\nu_{nm} = \Delta E_{nm} = E_n - E_m \tag{82}$$

where E_n and E_m represent the energies of two states of the whole molecular system in the magnetic field and between which magnetic dipole transitions are allowed. The selection rules for this are (K39, C16)

$$\Delta m = 0, \pm 1 \qquad \Delta F = 0, \pm 1 \qquad \Delta m_k = 0, \pm 1 \qquad (83)$$

where the first two equations apply in the presence of weak external magnetic fields and the last equation applies to each constituent magnetic moment when the external magnetic field is so strong that these moments are decoupled from each other.

For the detection of the occurrence of these reorientations, a beam of molecules is spread by an inhomogeneous magnetic field and refocused onto a detector by a subsequent inhomogeneous field. Since this refocusing depends merely on the effects of the two fields compensating each other and since any given molecule has the same velocity in both fields, this refocusing is not affected by the velocity distribution of the molecules. The transitions between states of different space quantization are produced in the homogeneous field of an electromagnet placed in the region between the two deflecting magnets. In the gap of this electromagnet is placed a loop of wire which is connected to a radiofrequency oscillator to produce the oscillating magnetic field. If a reorientation of a moment occurs in this field, the subsequent conditions in the second field are no longer correct for refocusing and the intensity at the detector decreases. Thus, if the beam intensity is observed at a fixed homogeneous magnetic field while the oscillator frequency is slowly varied, a "radiofrequency spectrum" of the molecule in the field will be obtained with minima of beam intensity occurring when the oscillator frequency equals the frequency of Eq. (82).

Figure 10 is a schematic diagram of a molecular beam apparatus with some typical molecular paths. The deflections in this figure are much exaggerated; the maximum deflection of a molecule with average velocity and a magnetic moment of a nuclear magneton is only about 0.05 mm in a typical molecular beam apparatus, even though the gradient of the magnetic field may be 80,000 gauss/cm. Because of these small deflections the defining slits at the source S, collimator, and detector D, respectively, must be very narrow, 0.01-mm widths being typical. Very low pressures, of the order of 10^{-7} mm Hg, must be maintained in the main chamber of the apparatus to prevent both small-angle scattering from weakening the beam and unsteadiness of the detector. Further details of apparatus design can be found in the two papers referred to above (R6, K9) and in several general reviews of molecular beam techniques by Fraser (F17, F18), Estermann (E5), Kellogg and Millman (K11), and Hamilton (H6).

The first experiments using this method were with $^1\Sigma$ diatomic molecules for which there was no permanent electron magnetic moment

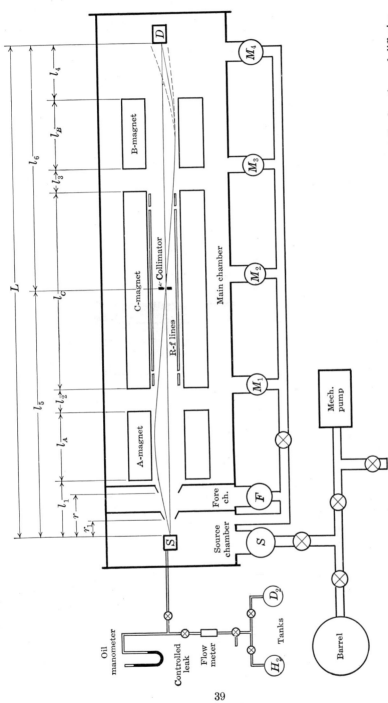

Fig. 10. Schematic diagram of a typical molecular beam apparatus. The symbols S, F, and M represent the locations of diffusion pumps. In a typical high-precision apparatus $l_C = 150$ cm.

39

and for which it was initially assumed that all intramolecular interactions could be neglected. With these assumptions, Eq. (20) becomes

$$W_M(m_I) = -\frac{\mu_I}{I}\mathbf{I}\cdot\mathbf{H}_0 = -\frac{\mu_I}{I}H_0 m_I \tag{84}$$

and with $\Delta m_I = \pm 1$

$$\nu_0 = \frac{\Delta W}{2\pi\hbar} = \frac{W_M(m_I) - W_M(m_I + 1)}{2\pi\hbar} = \frac{(\mu_I/I)H_0}{2\pi\hbar} \tag{85}$$

This is just the classical Larmor frequency. From Eq. (85) and from
measurements of the field strength H_0 and corresponding frequency
ν_0, μ_I/I is determined. Because of the importance of this relation it is
worth noting several other alternative but equivalent forms of writing
the fundamental Larmor relation, Eq. (85). These include

$$\omega_0 = 2\pi\nu_0 = \gamma_I H_0 \tag{86}$$

$$\nu_0 = \frac{g_I \mu_{NM}}{2\pi\hbar} H_0 \tag{87}$$

and, in numerical terms (D17), if H_0 is in gauss and ν_0 in cycles per
second,

$$\nu_0 = 762.30 g_I H_0 \tag{88}$$

A typical molecular beam magnetic resonance curve is shown in Fig.
11, where the beam intensity is plotted as a function of H_0.

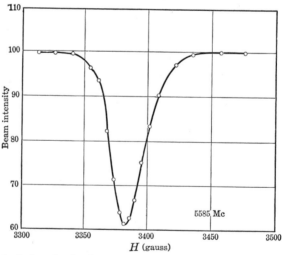

Fig. 11. A typical molecular beam resonance curve in nuclear magnetic moment
measurements. Li[7] nucleus in lithium chloride (R6).

The nature of the resonance reorientations of nuclear magnetic moments can be demonstrated in a particularly simple and informative manner with the use of a rotating coordinate system. Consider that one or more nuclei are present, all with the same gyromagnetic ratio γ_I, and that they are in the presence of an external magnetic field $\mathbf{H}$. Then the equation of motion for such a nuclear moment is

$$\hbar \frac{d\mathbf{I}}{dt} = \gamma_I \hbar \mathbf{I} \times \mathbf{H} \tag{89}$$

Now, however, consider this problem from the point of view of a coordinate system rotating with angular velocity $\boldsymbol{\omega}$. If $\partial \mathbf{I}/\partial t$ is the rate of charge of I relative to such a coordinate system,

$$\frac{d\mathbf{I}}{dt} = \frac{\partial \mathbf{I}}{\partial t} + \boldsymbol{\omega} \times \mathbf{I} \tag{90}$$

Hence in this rotating coordinate system the equation of motion is that resulting from the elimination of $d\mathbf{I}/dt$ between Eqs. (89) and (90), or

$$\frac{\partial \mathbf{I}}{\partial t} = \gamma_I \mathbf{I} \times \left(\mathbf{H} + \frac{\boldsymbol{\omega}}{\gamma_I} \right) \tag{91}$$

Hence for the rotating coordinate system the equation of motion is the same as for the fixed coordinate system except for the addition of a fictitious magnetic field $\boldsymbol{\omega}/\gamma_I$. Hence, if $\mathbf{H}_{\text{eff}}$ is the effective magnetic field in the rotating frame of reference,

$$\mathbf{H}_{\text{eff}} = \mathbf{H} + \frac{\boldsymbol{\omega}}{\gamma_I} \tag{92}$$

This result may be applied to the usual molecular beam resonance case where a nucleus of gyromagnetic ratio γ_I is in the presence of a fixed magnetic field $\mathbf{H}_0$ about which a weaker field $\mathbf{H}_1$ perpendicular to $\mathbf{H}_0$ rotates with angular frequency ω anti-parallel to $\mathbf{H}_0$. Now consider this from the point of view of a rotating coordinate system rotating with the angular velocity ω of $\mathbf{H}_1$ and let $\mathbf{k}$ be a unit vector parallel to $\mathbf{H}_0$ and $\mathbf{i}$ be a unit vector parallel to $\mathbf{H}_1$ as in Fig. 12, so that in the rotating coordinate system

$$\mathbf{H}_0 = H_0 \mathbf{k} \qquad \mathbf{H}_1 = H_1 \mathbf{i} \qquad \boldsymbol{\omega} = -\omega \mathbf{k} \tag{93}$$

Then, by Eq. (92), in the rotating frame of reference

$$\mathbf{H}_{\text{eff}} = \left(H_0 - \frac{\omega}{\gamma_I} \right) \mathbf{k} + H_1 \mathbf{i} \tag{94}$$

Hence the effective field is as in Fig. 12. At exact resonance, then, the $\mathbf{H}_{\text{eff}}$ is simply $H_1\mathbf{i}$, and a nucleus originally parallel to $\mathbf{H}_0$ will precess about $H_1\mathbf{i}$ relative to this coordinate system and change its orientation from parallel $\mathbf{H}_0$, to anti-parallel, back to parallel, etc. If, instead of being at exact resonance, one were just a little off resonance, as in Fig. 12, a nucleus originally parallel to $\mathbf{H}_0$ would precess around $\mathbf{H}_{\text{eff}}$ but

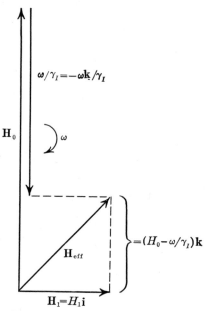

Fig. 12.   Effective magnetic field in the rotating coordinate system.

would never be exactly anti-parallel to H_0. A measure of the width of the resonance could be the frequency shift for $\mathbf{H}_{\text{eff}}$ to be at a $45°$ angle, since then the nucleus can precess only from parallel to $\mathbf{H}_0$ to perpendicular to it. From Eq. (94) this occurs when

$$H_0 - \frac{\omega}{\gamma_I} = H_1 \tag{95}$$

or if $\omega_0 = 2\pi\nu_0 = \gamma_I H_0$. This occurs for

$$\omega_0 - \omega = \gamma_I H_1 = \frac{\omega_0 H_1}{H_0} \tag{96}$$

Hence the full width at half value will be approximately

$$\Delta\omega = \frac{2\omega_0 H_1}{H_0} \tag{97}$$

However, if H_1 is of sufficient strength to produce complete reorientation at exact resonance in the time t that the molecule is exposed to the
oscillating field, i.e., to produce a reorientation of π radians about H_1,

$$\pi = \omega_{H_1}t = \gamma_I H_1 t \tag{98}$$

If this is used in Eq. (97),

$$\Delta\omega = \frac{2\pi\omega_0}{\gamma_I H_0}\frac{1}{t} = \frac{2\pi}{t} \tag{99}$$

or

$$\Delta\nu = \frac{1}{t} \tag{100}$$

It should be noted that this frequency spread is of just the magnitude
that would be expected from a Fourier analysis of a sine wave turned
on for only a time t.

The exact quantum-mechanical transition probability in this case
has been calculated by Rabi (R5, R6, R13) with the following result.
If $P_{-\frac{1}{2} \leftarrow \frac{1}{2}}$ is the probability for a transition from a state with $m = \frac{1}{2}$
to $m = -\frac{1}{2}$ when $I = \frac{1}{2}$,

$$P_{-\frac{1}{2} \leftarrow \frac{1}{2}} = \sin^2\Theta\sin^2\tfrac{1}{2}at \tag{101}$$

where

$$\sin\Theta = \frac{2b}{a} \qquad \cos\Theta = \frac{\omega_0 - \omega}{a}$$

$$a = [(\omega_0 - \omega)^2 + (2b)^2]^{\frac{1}{2}} \qquad \omega_0 = 2\pi\nu_0 = \gamma_I H_0 \tag{102}$$

$$2b = \gamma_I H_1 = \frac{\omega_0 H_1}{H_0}$$

This may be extended to any spin I with the same gyromagnetic ratio
by using a formula due to Majorana (M4):

$$P_{m' \leftarrow m} = \left(\cos\frac{\alpha}{2}\right)^{4I}(I + m)!(I + m')!(I - m)!(I - m')!$$

$$\times \left[\sum_{\lambda=0}^{2I}\frac{(-1)^\lambda(\tan\tfrac{1}{2}\alpha)^{2\lambda-m+m'}}{(\lambda - m + m')!(I + m - \lambda)!(I - m' - \lambda)!}\right]^2 \tag{103}$$

where α is defined by $\sin^2(\alpha/2) = P_{-\frac{1}{2} \leftarrow \frac{1}{2}}$ and where any term containing factorials of negative numbers is to be omitted.

Although Eq. (101) applies directly to H_1 rotating about H_0, it can
also to a very good approximation be applied to an oscillating field
provided (B16) H_1 is replaced by one-half the amplitude of the oscillating field; this is a reasonable result since an oscillating field can be
thought of as the resultant of two fields of one-half the amplitude rotat-

ing in opposite directions, and the field rotating opposite to the Larmor precession is not in resonance and so produces a negligible effect. One unfortunate effect of replacing a rotating field by an oscillating one is that the possibility of determining the sign of the moment by measuring the direction of the Larmor precession is lost, since it is impossible to tell which of the two equivalent rotating fields produces a transition. However, Millman (M18) has pointed out that in actual experiments there exists a slight rotating component of known direction as a result of certain end effects of the oscillating field; this field may be used in the determination of the sign of the moment.

Torrey (T19), using Eq. (101) and averaging over the Maxwellian velocity distribution in the beam, has shown that the resonance width with an oscillating current to give maximum transition probability at exact resonance is given by $t \, \Delta\nu = 1.07$, where t is the time spent in the field by the molecule of most probable velocity. This is almost exactly the same as the approximate value of $t \, \Delta\nu = 1$ estimated above in Eq. (101).

In actual practice the above resonance width frequently cannot be achieved owing to the impossibility of obtaining a sufficiently homogeneous magnetic field over the entire length of the oscillating field region. Ramsey (R13), however, has recently developed a new molecular beam technique which overcomes the effect of field inhomogeneities in adding to the resonance width and which in addition produces resonances that are 40 percent narrower than those of the old method, even in a perfectly homogeneous magnetic field. In the new method the oscillating magnetic field is not introduced throughout the entire length of the homogeneous magnetic field, but instead a much stronger oscillating field is used only at the beginning and the end of the homogeneous field as shown in Fig. 10. This method can most easily be understood in terms of the above-mentioned procedure in which the problem is considered from the point of view of a coordinate system rotating with the rotating (or oscillating) magnetic field. In such a coordinate system near resonance, the nuclei in the first oscillating field precess about H_1. If then the mean nuclear precession frequency about H_0 in the intermediate region is equal to the oscillator frequency, the nucleus in the intermediate region will undergo no net precession relative to the rotating coordinate system and will enter the second oscillating field with the same orientation relative to H_1 as that with which it left the first. Hence in the second oscillating field it will exactly double its angle of precession about H_1. This will be true regardless of the velocity of the molecule and, hence, the length of time that the molecule is in the magnetic field. This condition is the most favorable for producing the maximum transition probability. If, on the other hand, the oscillator frequency is not exactly equal to the mean precession frequency, the nucleus will enter the second oscillating field region with an orientation relative to H_1 which is different from that on leaving the first and which, when averaged over the molecular velocity distribution, is less

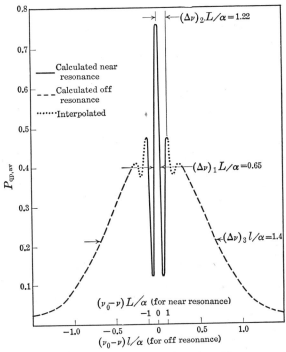

Fig. 13. Theoretical transition probability as a function of frequency with separated oscillating fields method. Solid line, calculated near resonance; broken line, calculated off resonance; dotted line, interpolated. l = length of oscillating fields. L = separation of oscillating fields. α = most probable molecular velocity (R13).

favorable to a maximum reorientation by H_1. Therefore there should be a maximum transition probability when the oscillator frequency is exactly equal to the mean precession frequency of the nuclei in the intermediate region. Since the position of the resonance is dependent only on the mean precession frequency of the nuclei and not on the instantaneous frequencies, the resonance is not broadened by inhomogeneities of the magnetic field. This is the greatest advantage of the new method. Ramsey (R13) has calculated the theoretical transition probability for the new method and finds, corresponding to Eq. (101),

$$P_{-\frac{1}{2} \leftarrow \frac{1}{2}} = 4 \sin^2 \Theta \sin^2 \tfrac{1}{2}a\tau(\cos \tfrac{1}{2}\lambda T \cos \tfrac{1}{2}a\tau - \cos \Theta \sin \tfrac{1}{2}\lambda T \sin \tfrac{1}{2}a\tau)^2$$

$$(104)$$

where τ is the length of time the molecule is in each of the oscillating field regions, T is the time it is in the intermediate region, $\lambda = \bar{\omega}_0 - \omega$, and the other quantities are as in Eq. (102). When this is averaged over the velocity distribution of the molecules, the result is as in Fig. 13. This theoretical prediction can be compared to the experimental results of Kolsky, Phipps, Ramsey, and Silsbee (K18) on D_2 shown in Fig. 14.

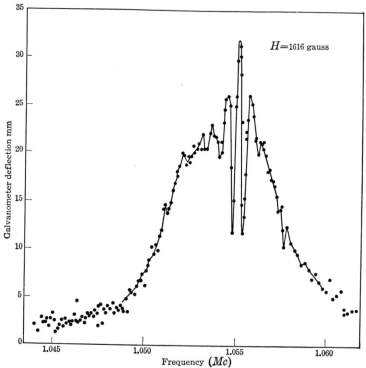

Fig. 14.   Experimental transition probability as a function of frequency with separated oscillating fields method (K18).

The virtue of the new method is clearly shown in Fig. 14, since, with the field homogeneity obtainable in that experiment, the broad background peak is about as sharp as the sharpest resonances obtainable by the old method, whereas the superposed sharp resonances with the new method are many times narrower. Ramsey and Silsbee (R16a) have shown that by introducing various relative phase shifts between the two oscillating fields even greater improvements in the precision can be obtained.

Magnitudes and signs of nuclear magnetic moments have been measured for a large number of nuclei with the molecular beam resonance method. Figure 11 is typical of the resonance curves obtained. The numerical results of these experiments are included in the tables of Section 4C.

In studying H_2, D_2, and HD in this way Kellogg, Rabi, Ramsey, and Zacharias (K9, K8, R10) found marked structure. Figure 15 is typical

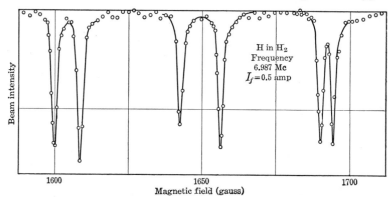

H in H_2
Frequency
6.987 Mc
$I_f = 0.5$ amp

Beam intensity

1600   1650   1700
Magnetic field (gauss)

Fig. 15.   Molecular beam radiofrequency spectrum of ortho-H_2 molecules arising
from transitions of the resultant nuclear spin (K9).

of their experimental results on H_2. Although it was found possible to account fully for the results with H_2 by assuming purely magnetic interactions, this proved impossible with molecules containing the deuteron, as illustrated in Fig. 16, where the dotted lines at the top of

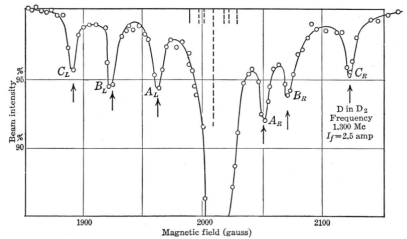

Beam intensity

C_L B_L A_L B_R A_R C_R

95 %
90 %

D in D_2
Frequency
1.300 Mc
$I_f = 2.5$ amp

1900   2000   2100
Magnetic field (gauss)

Fig. 16.   Radiofrequency spectrum of D_2 at 80°K arising from transitions of the
resultant nuclear spin. Dotted lines indicate spectrum predicted on assumption of
no deuteron electrical quadrupole moment. Arrows indicate spectrum predicted
on assumption of suitable quadrupole moment (K8).

the figure show the spectrum to be expected from magnetic interactions alone. However, by making the additional important assumption that the deuteron possesses an electrical quadrupole moment, all results could be fully accounted for. In these experiments a total of more than fifty different resonance minima were observed along with the dependence of the positions of some of these minima on external magnetic field; yet all the results could be fully accounted for by assuming the Hamiltonian of the orientation dependent interaction of the different $^1\Sigma$ hydrogen molecules to be of the following form (corresponding to Fig. 17):

$$\mathfrak{H} = -\mathbf{\mu}_1\cdot\mathbf{H}[1 - \sigma_1(\mathbf{J})] - \mathbf{\mu}_2\cdot\mathbf{H}[1 - \sigma_2(\mathbf{J})] - \mathbf{\mu}_R\cdot\mathbf{H}[1 - \sigma_J(\mathbf{J})]$$

$$- H_1{}'(\mathbf{\mu}_1\cdot\mathbf{J}) - H_2{}'(\mathbf{\mu}_2\cdot J) + \frac{1}{r^3}\left[\mathbf{\mu}_1\cdot\mathbf{\mu}_2 - \frac{3(\mathbf{\mu}_1\cdot\mathbf{r})(\mathbf{\mu}_2\cdot\mathbf{r})}{r^2}\right]$$

$$- \frac{1}{2}\xi_{m,J}H^2 + \sum_{k=1}^{2}\frac{e^2 q_{Jk}Q_k}{2I_k(2I_k - 1)J(2J - 1)}$$

$$[3(\mathbf{I}_k\cdot\mathbf{J})^2 + \tfrac{3}{2}\mathbf{I}_k\cdot\mathbf{J} - \mathbf{I}_k{}^2\mathbf{J}^2] \quad (105)$$

The first three terms correspond to the interaction of the two nuclear and one rotational magnetic moments with the external field; cf. Eq. (18). The $[1 - \sigma]$ factors are the corrections introduced by Ramsey (R14, R16, R17) for the magnetic shielding of the nuclei as discussed on page 72. The fourth and fifth terms correspond to the interaction of the nuclear magnetic moments with the magnetic field produced by the rotation of the molecule; cf. Eq. (21). The sixth term corresponds to the magnetic interaction of the two nuclear magnetic moments. The seventh term corresponds to the diamagnetic interaction of the electrons of the molecule with the external field (R12a). The last term cor-

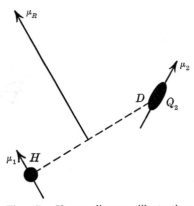

Fig. 17.　Vector diagram illustrating relevant moments in HD molecule.

responds to the assumed nuclear electrical quadrupole moment interacting with the inhomogeneous electric field of the rest of the molecule; cf. Eq. (8). The Hamiltonian, Eq. (105), can serve to predict the energy levels of the molecule if Section 2C is used to provide the matrix elements and, if the perturbation theory of secular equation solution is used, to find the energy levels. This theoretical problem is treated in detail by Kellogg, Rabi, Ramsey, and Zacharias (K9, K8) and by Ramsey (R10). More accurate measurements on these molecules are now being made with the new and more sensitive separated oscillating field method by Kolsky, Phipps, Ramsey, and Silsbee (K18). Figure 18 is a typical curve obtained with the new method. The molecular structure significance of these results is discussed in Section 5.

The hydrogen molecules in the above work have the great advantage that at the liquid-air temperatures of the source only the first rotational state is excited, so that the number of rotational states is sufficiently few that the individual spectral lines can be resolved. However, effects attributable to a nuclear quadrupole moment have been found by Kusch and Millman (K39), Nierenberg and Ramsey (N8), and others in several heavier diatomic molecules. A statistical theory of quadrupole interactions for large J has been developed by Feld and Lamb (F6), Foley (F11), Ramsey (R11, R17a), and others, which agrees well with the experimental results. By using this theory the values of $q_J Q$ can be calculated and the nuclear spin determined from the experimental curves.

The resonance method has also been applied by Kusch, Millman, and Rabi (K39, K40) to the study of atoms possessing an electron as well as a nuclear magnetic moment. The energy levels for such an atom are given by Eq. (36) and are plotted in Fig. 4. Hence resonance minima occur for transitions which are allowed by the selection rules of Eq. (83). In this way the hyperfine structure of a number of atoms has been investigated with great precision. From these experiments the hyperfine structure separation $\Delta\nu$ of Eq. (37) is obtained, and hence μ_I can be calculated. The number of spectral lines observed also determines the spin. Measurements on a number of atoms have been made in this way. Of particular interest has been the measurement of the spin of the isotope K^{40}, which is present in only one part in 8600, by Zacharias (Z2) and the measurement of $\Delta\nu$ in the hydrogen and deuterium atoms by a group working with Rabi (N1, N2, P26a) and another group with Zacharias (N3).

Although the precision of relative values of nuclear moments can be very high indeed by the resonance method because only the measurement of frequency ratios is involved, the determination of absolute values has been difficult because of the difficulty in measuring the absolute value of the magnetic field in any one experiment. Millman and Kusch (M22) sought to overcome this difficulty by calibrating the magnetic field in terms of the electron magnetic moment and by assuming that the electron magnetic moment was exactly 1 Bohr magneton.

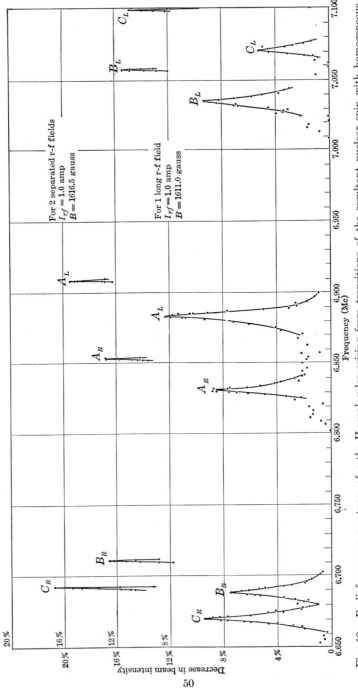

Fig. 18. Radiofrequency spectrum of ortho-H₂ molecules arising from transitions of the resultant nuclear spin with homogeneous magnetic field 150 cm long. Lower peaks with original method. Upper peaks with separated oscillating field method (K18).

For 2 separated r-f fields
$I_{rf} = 1.0$ amp
$B = 1616.5$ gauss

For 1 long r-f field
$I_{rf} = 1.0$ amp
$B = 1611.0$ gauss

Frequency (Mc)

Decrease in beam intensity

This calibration is possible in an atomic experiment of the type of the preceding paragraph, since the effectiveness of an external magnetic field in producing a given stage of intermediate coupling in Fig. 4 depends, by Eq. (37), on

$$x = \frac{(-\mu_J/J + \mu_I/I)H}{2\pi\hbar\,\Delta\nu} \tag{106}$$

where the second term in the numerator is only a small correction easily approximated by the measured value of μ_I with approximately calibrated fields. By observing the experimental spectrum of an atom whose hyperfine structure separation $\Delta\nu$ has previously been measured, x is determined; therefore from the above and the value of $\Delta\nu$, H can be found in terms of the electron magnetic moment μ_J. However, when the experiments (N1, N2, N3) on the hydrogen $\Delta\nu$ mentioned in the preceding paragraph were performed, a disagreement was found with the value calculated from the proton magnetic moment obtained by measurements in which the above field calibration was used. It was suggested by Breit (B38) and Schwinger (S37) that this discrepancy might be due to the electron magnetic moment being slightly different from 1 Bohr magneton. Kusch, Foley, and Mann (K42, M7) therefore performed a similar experiment with different atoms in $^2S_{1/2}$, $^2P_{1/2}$, and $^2P_{3/2}$ states to see if different results would be obtained corresponding to the fact that in a $P_{1/2}$ state the resultant electron magnetic moment is the difference between an orbital and spin contribution whereas in the $P_{3/2}$ state it is the sum of the two contributions. They found that there was indeed a difference and that it was consistent with the theoretical value of the anomalous electron moment as calculated by Schwinger (S37). Subsequently Koenig, Prodell, and Kusch (K15a) measured the magnetic moment of the $^2S_{1/2}$ state of atomic hydrogen in terms of the proton magnetic moment. When this is combined with the experimental result of Gardner and Purcell (G2), which gives the proton magnetic moment in terms of the Bohr magneton as described in Section 4A, the value of the spin magnetic moment of the electron is determined to be (1.001145 ± 0.000013) Bohr magnetons. Schwinger's (S37) value for this with a second-order calculation is 1.00116. From a fourth-order calculation Karplus and Kroll (K4) have shown the theoretical value to be $1 + \alpha/2\pi - 2.973\alpha^2/\pi^2 = 1.0011454$. The agreement is most striking and is evidence for the validity of a higher-order quantum electrodynamical calculation. These experiments also provide an absolute calibration of the magnetic fields in which nuclear moments are measured. However, other methods have also been devised recently. All of these will be discussed in Section 4A.

Various modifications of the molecular beam resonance methods from those described above are possible and have been used. For example, the fields can be set to refocus an atom which does undergo a transition instead of an atom which undergoes no resonance transition. Likewise, the methods have recently been applied to electric deflections and electric transitions (H18, T31). Nuclear electrical quadrupole moment interactions have been detected with such an electric resonance method. Experiments on excited atomic states are possible (ZR1).

The chief experimental difficulty with the molecular beam technique is that of obtaining suitable substances that can effectively be detected by the molecular beam detectors. The most effective detector has been a surface ionization detector which relies on the fact that an atom with a sufficiently low ionization potential will give up an electron if it strikes a heated wolfram (tungsten) or oxide-coated wolfram wire, after which the charged ion can be measured electrically. However, this method has so far been applicable only to molecules containing lithium, sodium, potassium, calcium, rubidium, indium, gallium, aluminum, and barium. Nevertheless, many other nuclei have been studied in this way with the use of complex molecules containing the nucleus of interest and one of the above atoms. Recently an extension of this method has been achieved by Zacharias (D7), who finds that chlorine can gain an electron on striking a heated wolfram wire. He also found that the sensitivity of the method could be markedly improved by analyzing the particles with a mass spectrometer after they pass through the molecular beam apparatus. Hin Lew has successfully ionized other atoms such as boron by electron bombardment before they pass through a subsequent analyzing spectrometer. The other detector that has been used most in molecular beams studies is the Stern-Pirani (F17, F18) detector, which relies on the change in temperature of a hot wire in a small chamber in which the detected molecules accumulate. This detector is much less sensitive than the other but is the only one so far applicable to the important case of molecular hydrogen. Recently, the radioactivity of radioactive atoms in a molecular beam has been used as an effective detector (S45b).

Applications of the molecular beam resonance method to the study of molecular structure are discussed in Section 5.

E. Neutron Beam Resonance Method

A method very similar in principle to the molecular beam resonance method has been used by Bloch and Alvarez (A1) and later by Roberts (A8) and Bloch (B24) and their co-workers to measure the magnetic moment of the neutron. In this experiment the deflecting and refocusing magnetic fields of the molecular beam resonance method are replaced by two magnetized iron plates through which the beam passes. As first pointed out by Bloch (B15), a neutron beam passing through a magnetized ferromagnetic substance will become partially polarized as a result of the interference between the nuclear scattering and the magnetic scattering caused by the magnetic interaction of the neutron magnetic moment with the atomic magnetic moment. The theory has been improved by Schwinger (S35) and Halpern and Holstein (H3).

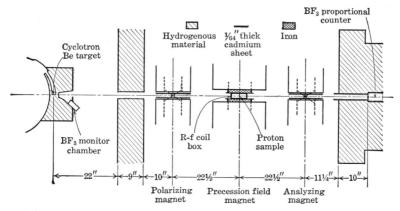

Fig. 19.   Experimental arrangement for a typical neutron beam magnetic resonance experiment (B24).

It is very important, as has been experimentally verified (B17, B19, H17), that the iron be magnetically highly saturated. Since the transmitted neutron beam is partially polarized, two such plates magnetized in the same direction can be used as a polarizer and analyzer to detect when resonance reorientations occur between them; since the total transmitted beam intensity will then drop. Recently it has become possible to produce even more highly polarized beams by reflecting neutrons from a magnetized sheet of cobalt (H19). A typical apparatus is shown in Fig. 19.

In the most recent and most precise measurements (A8, B24), the ratio of the neutron moment to the proton moment was very accurately determined by also measuring the proton moment at the same time by the resonance absorption and induction methods discussed in Section 3F. The results of these measurements are discussed in Section 4.

This technique combined with the precision method of separated oscillating fields has been used by Smith, Ramsey, and Purcell (S45) to set an upper limit to the electrical dipole moment of the neutron.

F. Nuclear Resonance Absorption and Induction Methods [1]

In the molecular beam resonance method the occurrence of resonance is detected by the effect of the transition on the molecules. Recently, however, Purcell, Torrey, and Pound (P27) and Bloch, Hansen, and Packard (B18) in independent but closely related experiments have succeeded in detecting the occurrence of resonance by the induced electromotive force due to the reorientation of the nuclei at resonance. The possibility of such experiments was first suggested by Gorter (G14, G15) at a much earlier date, but his early experiments were unfortunately not successful.

One inherent feature of these experiments is that absorption of radiation is largely canceled by stimulated emission; only in so far as the lower energy levels are more abundantly occupied than the higher ones is there any net effect. Even if the nuclear spins are in complete thermal equilibrium, this means that only a small fraction of the nuclei have an uncanceled effect. For example, with hydrogen the fractional difference is just $e^{2\mu_I H/kT} - 1 \sim 10^{-5}$ at room temperature and 7000 gauss.

Purcell's method, in its original conception, was essentially a magnetic resonance absorption method in that he observed the absorption of energy from a coil carrying an oscillating current when the frequency of the oscillator equaled the Larmor frequency, Eq. (85), of the nuclei or some other Bohr frequency, Eq. (82), for which a transition is allowed.

Bloch's method, in its original conception, however, was more appropriately described as a magnetic resonance induction method. Two coils were used at right angles to each other in such a way that there was little pick-up between the two coils. Through one coil an oscillating current was passed while the other was connected to a sensitive receiver. As discussed in Section 3D, an oscillating magnetic field is equivalent to two rotating fields of one-half the amplitude rotating in opposite directions. Near resonance the equivalent field rotating in the same direction as the Larmor precession is much more effective in causing the magnetization of the nuclei to follow it. Consequently, near resonance the magnetization rotates in that direction at the frequency of the oscillating field and induces a signal in the receiver coil. This induced signal was a maximum at the resonance frequency in one form of the experiment.

As the two methods have developed, they have become essentially very similar. A typical block diagram of the apparatus used for resonance studies by Purcell (B26) is shown in Fig. 20. A detailed descrip-

---

[1] These methods are also referred to as nuclear paramagnetic resonance.

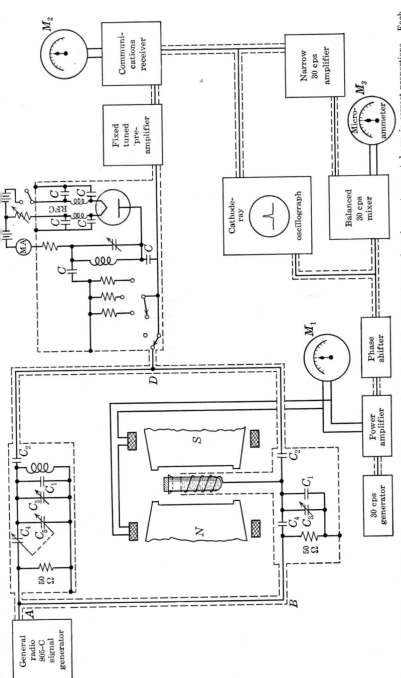

Fig. 20. Block diagram of circuit for nuclear magnetic resonance absorption experiments. The sample and magnet are not drawn in correct proportions. Each of the two branches following A contains a resonant circuit, and one includes a coil surrounding the sample (the return lead from the coil is via the indicated ground circuit). The line AB contains an extra half wavelength, so that a voltage node is produced at D if the bridge is perfectly balanced. When the magnetic field is swept through a nuclear resonance, the balance is disturbed and a signal produced on the oscillograph and M_3. A circuit used for noise figure measurements precedes the pre-amplifier (B26).

tion of these and other detection techniques has recently been given by Pound (ZP9).

Quantitative theories of these experiments have been worked out by Bloch (B20), Purcell (B26), Van Vleck (V3), and others. In these theories it is necessary to take into account the magnetic and electric quadrupole interactions of nuclei with their neighbors, with other magnetic substances, and with the elastic vibrations of the medium, since the resonance widths and the time required for the spins to reach thermal equilibrium are dependent on these. So far this has been done only in various approximate ways which are applicable to many but not all of the cases. One of the methods due to Bloch (B20) consolidates the effects of all these interactions into two empirical "relaxation times," i.e., exponential decay times for various components of magnetization to reach their equilibrium values. The two relevant relaxation times are the longitudinal or thermal relaxation time T_1 and the transverse relaxation time T_2. Because of this great simplification of the actual complex state of affairs, this treatment is necessarily only approximate.

The first of these relaxation times corresponds to the establishment of thermal equilibrium between the nuclear spins and the elastic vibrations of the material; it is defined in the absence of an oscillating field by

$$\dot{M}_z = -\frac{M_z - M_0}{T_1} \tag{107}$$

where M_z is the z component of $\mathbf{M}$, the resultant magnetization of the nuclear moments per unit volume, and M_0 is the equilibrium value of M_z when $H_z = H_0$. From Curie's law applied to the nuclear magnetic susceptibility with $\mu_I H_0 / I \ll kT$, M_0 is given by

$$M_0 = \chi_0 H_0 = \frac{I(I+1)(\mu_I/I)^2}{3kT} N_0 H_0 \tag{108}$$

where N_0 is the number of nuclei per unit volume.

The transverse relaxation time T_2 corresponds to the relaxation of M_x and M_y to their equilibrium value zero. T_2 is frequently less than T_1, since there is no problem of energy dissipation because the transverse components have no interaction energy with the field H_0. T_2 is defined in the absence of external magnetic fields by

$$\dot{M}_x = -\frac{M_x}{T_2} \qquad \dot{M}_y = -\frac{M_y}{T_2} \tag{109}$$

In the presence of an external magnetic field $\mathbf{H}$ the resultant magnetic moment $\mathbf{M}$ is also changed owing to the torque $\mathbf{M} \times \mathbf{H}$ exerted

on $\mathbf{M}$ and its associated angular momentum $\mathbf{M}/\gamma$. The combination
of all the above sources of rate of change of M give

$$\dot{\mathbf{M}} - \gamma(\mathbf{M} \times \mathbf{H}) + \frac{M_x}{T_2}\mathbf{i} + \frac{M_y}{T_2}\mathbf{j} + \frac{(M_z - M_0)}{T_1}\mathbf{k} = 0 \quad (110)$$

If the oscillating field is

$$H_x = 2H_1 \cos \omega t \qquad H_y = 0 \tag{111}$$

then near resonance, as discussed several times above, it is equivalent in
polarizing the medium to a field of amplitude H_1 rotating in the direction of the Larmor precession, i.e., if the nuclear moment is positive
the effective value of $\mathbf{H}$ in magnetizing the substance is

$$\mathbf{H} = H_1 \cos \omega t \mathbf{i} - H_1 \sin \omega t \mathbf{j} + H_0\mathbf{k} \tag{112}$$

The steady-state solution of Eqs. (110) and (112) is

$$M_x = \frac{M_0(\omega_0 H_1/H_0)[(\omega_0 - \omega) \cos \omega t + (1/T_2) \sin \omega t]}{(\omega - \omega_0)^2 + 1/T_2{}^2 + (\omega_0 H_1/H_0)^2(T_1/T_2)}$$

$$M_y = \frac{M_0(\omega_0 H_1/H_0)[1/T_2 \cos \omega t - (\omega_0 - \omega) \sin \omega t]}{(\omega - \omega_0)^2 + 1/T_2{}^2 + (\omega_0 H_1/H_0)^2(T_1/T_2)} \tag{113}$$

$$M_z = \frac{M_0[(\omega - \omega_0)^2 + (1/T_2{}^2)]}{(\omega - \omega_0)^2 + 1/T_2{}^2 + (\omega_0 H_1/H_0)^2(T_1/T_2)}$$

where ω_0 is the Larmor angular frequency $g_I \mu_{NM} H_0/\hbar$. That Eq. (113)
satisfies Eqs. (110) and (112) is easily checked directly by substitution.

　　The power absorption per unit volume from the oscillating field is
then given by the following, where H_x comes from Eq. (111) and M_x
from Eq. (113):

$$P(\omega) = \frac{\omega}{2\pi} \int_0^{2\pi/\omega} \dot{M}_x H_x \, dt = \frac{M_0\omega_0\omega H_1{}^2/H_0 T_2}{(\omega - \omega_0)^2 + 1/T_2{}^2 + (\omega_0 H_1/H_0)^2(T_1/T_2)}$$

$$\tag{114}$$

This shows that the power absorption goes through a resonance maximum when $\omega = \omega_0$ whose width and intensity are determined by $1/T_2$,
$\omega_0 H_1/H_0$, and T_1/T_2. This result is descriptive of many Purcell-type
experiments. However, in some of his experiments the oscillating field
is so weak and the relaxation time T_1 is so long compared to the time

of sweeping through resonance that, contrary to the steady-state assumption in the derivation of Eq. (113), equilibrium between the induced transitions and this relaxation process is not reached. A theory applicable in this limit and taking more detailed account of the various interactions has been given by Bloembergen, Purcell, and Pound (B26),

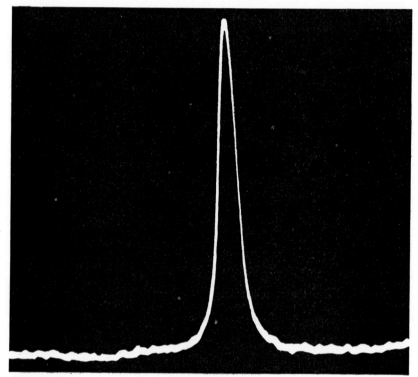

Fig. 21. Proton resonance (absorption) curve in ferric nitrate solution by Purcell method (B26).

Van Vleck (V3), and Bloch (B20). However, when Purcell's method is adjusted for maximum sensitivity in measuring nuclear moments, Eq. (113) applies. If H_1 in Eq. (114) is so small that the last term in the denominator can be neglected, the integral of $P(\omega)\, d\omega$ over the resonance is independent of T_2 and depends on M_0. By Eq. (108) M_0 depends in turn on the spin, so from this measurement a determination of the spin is possible in favorable cases. A typical proton resonance curve obtained by Purcell is shown in Fig. 21.

The voltage induced in the receiver coil of Bloch's experiment may also be evaluated from Eq. (113). The voltage induced per unit volume of substance in a tight-fitting coil of area A and N turns, since $B_y = 4\pi M_y$, is

$$V = -\frac{1}{c}\dot{B}_y NA = -\frac{4\pi}{c} NA\dot{M}_y$$

$$= \frac{(4\pi/c)NAM_0(\omega_0\omega H_1/H_0)[(\omega_0 - \omega)\cos\omega t + 1/T_2 \sin\omega t]}{(\omega - \omega_0)^2 + 1/T_2{}^2 + (\omega_0 H_1/H_0)^2(T_1/T_2)} \quad (115)$$

The method of detecting the signal induced in the coils may be made to be such as to detect the $\cos\omega t$ or the $\sin\omega t$ component or a combina-

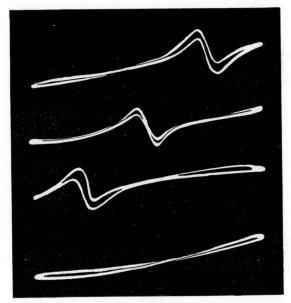

Fig. 22. Proton resonance (induction) curve in ferric nitrate solution by Bloch method (B18).

tion of these. If the $\cos\omega t$ term is detected, it can be seen from Eq. (115) that the result will be in the form of a dispersion curve as illustrated by the experimental curve in Fig. 22. However, in many of Bloch's experiments the above assumption of a complete steady state is not applicable. In particular he often uses relatively strong oscillating magnetic fields and sweeps through the resonance so rapidly that the relaxation times are not adequate to establish equilibrium. A transient solution to Eq. (110) can, however, be found corresponding to this case with the result that at resonance the induced voltage passes a maximum more like Fig. 21.

Bloch (B20) has shown that, in the limit of maximum sensitivity, the sensitivity of the two methods are the same. From an independently derived version of Eq. (114) Pound (B26) has evaluated the maximum signal-to-noise power ratio to be

$$\frac{P_s}{P_n} = \frac{V_c Q_0 (\alpha \zeta)^2 h^4 N_0^2 \gamma_I^2 \nu_0^3 T_2 [I(I+1)]^2}{2304 (kT)^2 (kTBF) T_1} \tag{116}$$

where the symbols not previously defined are: V_c, the volume of the coil; Q_0, the Q of the circuit in which the coil is contained; α, approximately 1; ζ, the fraction of V_c occupied by sample; N_0, the number of relevant nuclei per cubic centimeter; B, the band width at the indicating instrument; and F, the effective over-all noise figure for the circuit (F19). The signal-to-noise ratio, Eq. (116), is strongly dependent on the magnetic moment both explicitly and implicitly. Thus the amplitude ratio, or square root of Eq. (116), with 1 cm³ of water at 15,000 gauss and a band width of 1 cps is 1.4×10^6 for the protons, whereas a 1-molar solution of nuclei whose moments are 0.1 nuclear magneton under the same circumstances gives a ratio of only 1.3. In the latter case, therefore, a very narrow band width must be used with a consequently very long searching time; this is one of the major evils of this method.

It is often convenient to interpret the above results in terms of the rotating coordinate system analysis described in Section 3D. In this analysis the effective magnetic field in the rotating coordinate system is that given by Eq. (92). However, owing to local molecular fields H_0 is slightly different for different nuclei; consequently, different nuclei will precess in $\mathbf{H}_{\text{eff}}$ at slightly different rates and tend to get out of phase with time. The length of time to get out of phase in this manner corresponds to T_2 above. Likewise, owing to interaction with the crystal lattice, etc., there will be a tendency for the nuclei which have precessed about H_{eff} to an orientation other than that corresponding to thermal equilibrium to return to the distribution corresponding to thermal equilibrium. The time constant for this is measured by the above T_1.

Various modifications of the above methods have been introduced by different observers. Torrey (T20), Hahn (H1), and others (B5a) have used pulsed oscillating fields. Torrey studied the transient signals as the pulsed radiofrequency field was applied, and Hahn observed the decay of the residual nuclear signal immediately after the pulsed oscillating field was turned off. This decay time corresponds to T_2. In later experiments Hahn (H2) observed some particularly interesting effects which he called spin echoes. In particular, he applied a short r-f pulse followed by another similar pulse a time τ later where $T_2 \ll \tau \ll T_1$. He then found at a time τ after the last pulse that the nuclei, whose r-f signal had already died out in time T_2 after the last pulse, suddenly emitted another r-f pulse. This so-called spin echo arises from the fact that, despite the relaxation corresponding to T_2, the perturbations from the two r-f pulses produce a coherent constructive interference effect a time τ after the second pulse equal to the separation between the two pulses. As described by Hahn (H2) in greater detail, the origin of the delayed constructive interference which gives rise to the spin echoes can be understood by considering a few special cases from the point of view of the above rotating coordinate system. Alternatively, the origin of the spin echo can be understood by considering the special case in which the first applied pulse is of just sufficient magnitude and duration to move the resultant magnetization from being parallel to the external magnetic field by a 90° angle so that it becomes perpendicular to same. After a further time T_2, however, owing to transverse relaxation phenomena or perhaps to field inhomogeneities the nuclear moments which were originally pointing in one direction in a plane perpendicular to the external field will be pointing in all directions in that plane. However, for lengths of time short compared to T_1, they will still remain in that plane. If at the time τ after the first pulse, a second pulse is applied whose magnitude (to simplify the discussion) is just double that of the original pulse, this entire plane will be rotated 180° (twice the original 90°). The nuclear moments will therefore tend to unwind their loss of phase resulting from the transverse relaxation phenomenon and will exactly unwind after a time τ, i.e., after the time in which they originally got out of phase. The method is somewhat analogous to having a number of runners all of whom run at different but constant speeds. If they were started in one direction, they would soon spread out because of their different speeds. However, if at a time τ after the start each runner simultaneously reversed his direction, one would find that at a time 2τ after the start all would be neatly drawn up abreast at the starting line. Figure 23 illustrates a spin echo.

Pound (P15) has extended the nuclear magnetic resonance absorption method to the measurement of nuclear electrical quadrupole moment interactions in crystals. The torques exerted by the crystalline electric fields give rise to changes in the nuclear precession frequencies, and from observations of these shifts the spins and quadrupole interactions can be inferred. Also he finds that he can infer some quadrupole interaction data from relaxation time measurements in certain crystals.

These methods prove valuable not only as a means of learning nuclear spin and quadrupole moment information but also as a means of studying crystalline structure as discussed in Section 5. The effect of the nuclear quadrupole moment in shifting the resonance lines is given by Eq. (39) above. The simplifications of this expression which can be achieved from the symmetry properties of the crystal are discussed by Pound (P15).

Kastler (K5) and Bitter (B13) have introduced optical means of observation of the occurrence of nuclear magnetic resonances by the

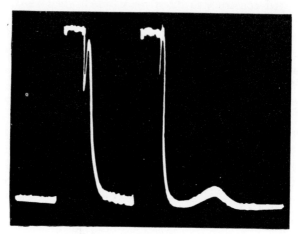

Fig. 23. Typical spin echo (H2).

changes in the intensity and polarization of light emitted by atoms in a magnetic field having an oscillatory component.

Ramsey and Pound (R16) have introduced a new resonance method, called nuclear audiofrequency spectroscopy by resonant heating of the nuclear spin system. This has been successfully applied to lithium fluoride which has such a long relaxation time T_1 that after the crystal is first placed in a strong magnetic field it takes of the order of 5 minutes for the nuclei to become aligned, as can be measured by the strength of the lithium resonance. If the crystal is removed from the field for a time short compared to 15 sec, however, the alignment can be immediately recovered when the crystal is reinserted in the strong field. It is found, however, that this property is destroyed if the sample is exposed to a suitable oscillatory magnetic field at about 60 kc while away from the strong field. The spectrum for destroying this property can be observed, and it measures the spin-spin interactions within the crystal lattice.

The resonance absorption and nuclear induction methods have been particularly favorable for high-precision measurements because the frequent collisions in liquids and high-density gases tend to average out the effects of the local molecular fields. When the collision frequency is large compared to the nuclear Larmor frequency, the local fields are partially averaged out and the width of the resonance becomes less than that to be expected from the local fields alone. This "collision narrowing" becomes more and more effective as the collision frequency increases. This phenomenon is discussed in greater detail in Sections 5F and 5G and in (B26). Although this "collision narrowing" is often an advantage, as in the precision measurement of nuclear magnetic moments, it is sometimes a disadvantage in that it precludes study of the local fields and interactions. For example, it prevents observations of the deuteron quadrupole moment in studies of deuterium molecules in a gas even though quadrupole effects can easily be observed with such molecules by the molecular beam methods.

The various nuclear induction methods have been used to measure a number of nuclear gyromagnetic ratios, quadrupole interactions, and spins as well as a number of molecular and solid state properties by Purcell, Bloch, Pound, Bitter, and others (e.g., B26, P12, P13, P14, B10, B23, P19, P20, P21, P23). Of particular interest have been the precision measurements of the ratios of the gyromagnetic ratios of the proton, neutron, deuteron, H^3, and He^3 in a series of experiments by Bloch (B24, B23, B22), Staub (B24), Roberts (A8), Bitter (B9), Anderson (A4, A5), Siegbahn (S41), and their associates. The results on nuclear moment measurements by this method are all summarized in Table 1 together with references to the original papers. This method has also been of great value in studying molecular and solid state problems which, however, are not directly relevant to nuclear physics. Furthermore, Pound (P15) studied nuclear electrical quadrupole interactions in crystals by this means. An extensive review article on the magnetic resonance absorption and induction methods has been written by Pake (P1). Chemical and solid state applications of these methods are given in Section 5.

Of particular interest has been the use of these methods in conjunction with other experiments to determine an absolute scale for nuclear moments. One of these is the experiment of Gardner and Purcell (G2). In this experiment the proton resonance was measured in the same magnetic field as the cyclotron frequency of the free electron, which should be $eH_0/2\pi mc$. Hence the ratio of these two frequencies directly gives the proton moment in Bohr magnetons. A related experiment by Hipple, Sommer, and Thomas (H15) measures the proton resonance frequency in terms of the cyclotron frequency of the proton. In a some-what different manner Bloch and his associates (B25) have also meas-ured the proton resonance frequency in terms of the cyclotron frequency of the proton. These two experiments therefore directly measure the proton moment in nuclear magnetons. In a still different experiment Thomas, Driscoll, and Hipple (T4) measured the resonance frequency of protons in a calibrated Bureau of Standards magnetic field. The results of these different measurements will be listed in Section 4 and compared with the closely related measurements of Kusch and his asso-ciates described in Section 3E.

Some data on nuclear spins have been obtained by Penrose (P9) and by Bleaney, Ingram, and Pryce (B14) by a quite different resonance method. They observe paramagnetic resonance, i.e., resonance of a diluted salt which has a resultant electronic angular momentum. By using sufficient magnetic dilution, they are able to find a hyperfine structure of the paramagnetic resonance which can be interpreted as an interaction between the ion and its nucleus. The spin of cobalt has been verified in this manner. A much more detailed discussion of para-magnetic resonance is given in Section 5R.

G. Microwave Spectroscopy Methods

A recently developed but very effective means of measuring nuclear spins, nuclear quadrupole interactions, and approximate values of nuclear magnetic moments is the study of the hyperfine structure of the microwave spectra of atoms and particularly of molecules at wave-lengths of the order of 1 cm. Although this method has not as yet pro-vided as much accuracy in the measurement of nuclear magnetic mo-ments as the methods of Section 3F, it is very effective in the measure-ment of spins and quadrupole interactions and it can be used with quite small amounts of materials since the much greater frequency leads to both greater transition probabilities and a more favorable Boltzmann factor.

In this method the nuclear effect is usually a hyperfine structure associated with some other energy transition in the molecule for which the Bohr frequency is in the microwave region.

Such microwave hyperfine structure effects with molecules were first observed by Good (G7, C12) with ammonia. This hyperfine structure has also been studied experimentally by Strandberg, Van Vleck, and Wilson (D1), Williams (W1), Gordy (S42), and their co-workers. With ammonia the nuclear electrical quadrupole interaction provides a hyperfine structure to the so-called inversion spectrum which arises from transitions between different states which exist by virtue of the possibility of the nitrogen atom going from one side to the other of the plane containing the three hydrogen atoms of NH_3. The wavelength corresponding to this transition is about 1 cm. The theory of the hyperfine structure resulting from a nuclear electrical quadrupole moment interaction in ammonia has been developed by Coles and Good (C12), Van Vleck (D1, V2), and associates.

In the microwave studies of Roberts, Beers, and Hill (R27) on atomic cesium the entire transition energy was due to a nuclear effect, i.e., the interaction between the cesium nuclear magnetic moment and the magnetic field of the electrons. This was possible because the hyperfine structure separation of the atomic ground state of Cs^{133} is 9192.6 Mc/sec or just in the microwave region. By the application of an external magnetic field the Zeeman effect on this line was studied.

A large number of linear and symmetric-top molecules have been studied whose rotational states have energies such that, for some of the allowed transitions between different rotational states, the energy differences correspond to convenient microwave wavelengths, usually of the order of 1 cm. Any large nuclear electrical quadrupole interaction which may exist will then produce a hyperfine structure from which the spin and quadrupole interaction can be inferred. Typical of these experiments has been the work on the linear triatomic molecules ClCN, BrCN, OCS, and ICN, and on the symmetric-top molecules CH_3I, CH_3Cl, and CH_3Br by Townes (T21, T24), Gordy (G8, G9, G10), Jen (J9, J10, J11), and their associates.

A typical apparatus for these experiments is shown in the block diagram of Fig. 24. For further details of microwave spectroscopic

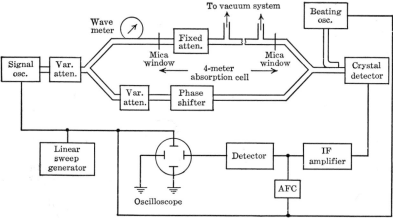

Fig. 24. Typical microwave spectrometer using radiofrequency bridge and heterodyne detection (T25).

techniques the reader is referred to the review articles of Gordy (G9) and of Townes and Schawlow (ZT4a). A typical experimental result compared with a first-order quadrupole interaction theory and a complete theory of the interaction is given in Fig. 25. A typical absorbing

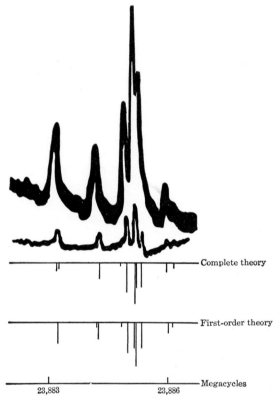

Fig. 25. Typical microwave spectrum showing comparison of portion of observed spectrum of $Cl^{35}CN$ with first-order and complete theories (B4).

gas pressure is 10^{-2} mm of mercury, at which low pressure the lines are approximately 1 mc wide.

The analysis of the microwave spectra for nuclear quadrupole interactions is similar to that described previously for studying such interactions in molecular beam experiments. However, in many of the microwave experiments symmetric-top instead of simple linear molecules are used. For these, in addition to the quantum number J, measuring the resultant rotational angular momentum $\mathbf{J}$, there is also a quantum number K for the projection $(\mathbf{J})_{z_0}$ of $\mathbf{J}$ along the molecular axis of symmetry. K takes on the values $K = 0, \pm 1, \cdots, \pm J$. With the use of K and with Eq. (15), Eq. (57) gives, for the quadrupole interaction energy E_Q,

$$E_Q = -eQ \frac{\partial^2 V^e}{\partial z_0{}^2} \left[1 - \frac{3K^2}{J(J+1)} \right] \frac{\frac{3}{8}C(C+1) - \frac{1}{2}I(I+1)J(J+1)}{I(2I-1)(2J-1)(2J+3)}$$

(117)

This was first derived by Coles and Good (C12) and Van Vleck (D1, V2). For a linear molecule K is necessarily zero, whence the above expression reduces, as it should, to that for linear molecules in Eq. (16). If more than one of the nuclei of the molecule have quadrupole moments the case becomes more complicated, but it has been analyzed by Bardeen and Townes (B4). The case of the asymmetric top has been discussed by Bragg (B33). Both nuclear spins and quadrupole interactions are obtained in these experiments.

Coles and Good (C12), Jen (J10, J12), Gordy (G9), and their associates have measured Zeeman effects in microwave spectra. In this way data for the first time have been obtained for the nuclear magnetic moments of I^{129} and S^{33}.

A more extensive section on microwave spectroscopy emphasizing applications to the study of molecular structure is given in Section 5Q.

H. Miscellaneous Methods

There are several methods of measuring nuclear spins which have so far been applicable to so few cases that they are merely briefly mentioned, references being given to the original work in which more details can be found.

One of these methods is the measurement of the rotational specific heat of hydrogen at very low temperatures; the theory was worked out by Dennison (D9, K29). As in the discussion of band spectra, hydrogen gas for which the two nuclei of the molecule are identical is essentially a mixture of two gases, orthohydrogen and parahydrogen. At low temperatures where kT is comparable to the spacing of the rotational energy levels, it is therefore reasonable to expect that this property should affect the specific heat of the gas. This it does, and from the experimental measurements it is possible both to identify which rotational states correspond to orthohydrogen and to measure the relative weights of the states. With these data and the results developed above in the discussion of band spectra, the spin and statistics of hydrogen may be found. The same measurements have been made in this way on D_2.

A historically important measurement of the ratio of the proton magnetic moment to that of the deuteron was made by Farkas (F1, F2) on the basis of a theory by Kalckar and Teller (K1) of the relative effectiveness of paramagnetic O_2 molecules in inducing conversion between the para and ortho states of hydrogen and of deuterium. As shown in the discussion of band spectra above, such a conversion from a para to an ortho state requires a spin dependent perturbation which is different for the two nuclei of the molecule. The inhomogeneous magnetic field of the O_2 electron moment provides such a perturbation. Its relative effectiveness in H_2 and in D_2 depends on the relative magnitudes of these two moments. Hence a comparison of these two rates of ortho-para conversion yields the magnetic moment ratio. If, on the other hand, a polar molecule like H_2O is used to induce the para-ortho transitions, its relative effectiveness on D_2 will be increased because, in addition to the magnetic effect, the inhomogeneous electric field of the polar molecule acting on the deuteron quadrupole moments can induce transitions. Casimir (C7) developed a theory applicable to the experiments of Farkas and Sandler (F3). He found good agreement between these experimental results and the molecular beam value of the deuteron quadrupole moment. This agreement has, however, recently been destroyed by a correction made to the theory by Hammermesh (H7) so that a repetition of the experiment would be highly desirable.

Another method of measuring spin and statistics which depends on the special symmetry properties required when two identical nuclei are present is to measure the Coulomb scattering of a particle by an identical nucleus, e.g., proton-proton scattering or the scattering of alpha-particles by helium. Mott (M25) first showed in the scattering of identical nuclei, even in the absence of specific nuclear forces, that the scattering should depart from the classical Rutherford-Darwin Coulomb scattering formula because of the above symmetry requirements on the wave function. This departure is large and easily observable (a factor of 2 for alpha-particles scattered at 45° by helium) and is dependent on both the spin and the statistics of the particle. The spin and statistics of alpha-particles and protons have been measured in this way by Gerthsen (G4) and others.

Another example of special methods is the measurement of the proton magnetic moment by Lasarew and Schubnikow (L3) from the nuclear paramagnetic susceptibility of hydrogen at very low temperatures. The dependence of such a magnetic susceptibility on the nuclear moment and temperature is given in Eq. (108). At temperatures of the order of 1°K this susceptibility becomes comparable to the diamagnetic susceptibility of the hydrogen molecule and hence measurable. However, just as in Stern's molecular beam method discussed above, there is a contribution to the paramagnetic susceptibility from the rotational magnetic moment; this correction is quite small, however, and can be made. As can be seen from Eq. (108), the result of these measurements is a determination of the magnetic moment of the proton. The results from this method agree with the more accurate results obtainable by other methods discussed above.

The above methods have so far not been applicable to an experimental determination of the spin of the neutron. However, as discussed by Schwinger (S36), an analysis of the experimental scattering of slow neutrons by ortho- and para-hydrogen indicates that the neutron spin is $\frac{1}{2}$.

Important spin information on radioactive nuclei has been obtained by studies of the angular correlation of successive beta- and gamma-rays. The radioactive half-lives, shapes of the beta-spectrum, and extent of internal conversion also contribute some spin information which in certain cases can be combined to determine spins of nuclear ground states (M12a). These methods have recently been reviewed and summarized by Feld (ZF5).

Recently, radioactive nuclei have been aligned by their interaction with external fields (G15b, D2a) and the departure from spherical symmetry of the emitted radiation has been observed. Experiments of this type in the future may be of value in giving information on moments of radioactive nuclei. Several methods of aligning nuclei have been proposed. The most obvious but experimentally most difficult is by merely allowing the nuclei to interact with an external magnetic field at very low temperatures (S41a). Gorter (G15a) and Rose (R32a) suggest the use of the magnetic interaction between the nuclei and the electrons with the electrons being aligned by an external magnetic field. Pound (P15) proposes an alignment which would take place as a result of the interaction of the nuclear electrical quadrupole moment with the crystalline field. Bleaney (B14d) suggests the use of the magnetic interaction between the nuclei and the electrons with the electrons being aligned by the crystalline field. At the moment of writing a possible small effect has been observed (G15b) with Gorter's method and a large $(44 \pm 5)\%$ effect has been observed by Daniels, Grace, and Robinson (D2a) using Bleaney's method.

4

RESULTS OF MEASUREMENTS OF NUCLEAR
MOMENTS AND STATISTICS

A. Results of Experiments to Determine an Absolute Scale for Nuclear Magnetic Moment Measurements

Most nuclear magnetic moment measurements by the methods of Section 3 finally involve the measurement of only a frequency and a magnetic field. Although high-precision frequency measurements are quite easy, high-precision magnetic field calibrations are very difficult. Consequently most nuclear moment measurements consist of a measurement of the ratio of the resonance frequency of an unknown and a known nucleus, usually hydrogen, in the same magnetic field. In this manner high-precision measurements of ratios of nuclear magnetic moments are easily possible. However, the determination of any one value with a high precision is very difficult. Nevertheless, as mentioned in Section 3, various observers have made measurements which contribute to a fixing of the absolute scales and which when combined also yield other nuclear and atomic data.

Rabi, Nafe, and Nelson (N1, N2), Nagle, Julian, and Zacharias (N3) and Prodell and Kusch (P26a) have measured the hyperfine structure separation $\Delta\nu_\mathrm{H}$, of the ground state of atomic hydrogen. They find $\Delta\nu_\mathrm{H} = 1420.4051 \pm 0.0003$ Mc. From this and the theory of such a separation given in Section 2, the value of the proton magnetic moment could be calculated, and hence such an experiment in principle would provide a standardization of the nuclear moment scale. Actually, however, when this is done it is found that the proton moment so determined disagrees with the values from the other methods listed below. As mentioned in Section 3, this has been interpreted as indicating that the electron spin magnetic moment differs slightly from 1 Bohr magneton.

Kusch, Foley, and Mann (K42, M7) in their experiments described in Section 3D determined the spin magnetic moment of the electron in Bohr magnetons. This result combined with the experiment of the preceding paragraph makes possible an absolute determination of the proton magnetic moment and hence a calibration of the magnetic moment scale. Since, however, such a calibration agrees within experimental error with those discussed below, the results of these experiments are most effectively combined with the other calibration experiments listed below and the theory for $\Delta\nu$ in Eqs. (24) and (30) to yield a more accurate value for the fine structure constant α by virtue of the appearance of α^2 in Eq. (24).

Taub and Kusch (T1) by the molecular beam experiment described in Section 3D have measured the proton magnetic moment in terms of the orbital magnetic moment of electrons in an atom and found $\mu_p/\mu_o = 0.00152106 \pm 0.005$ percent. Gardner and Purcell (G2) by the resonance absorption experiment previously described have measured the proton moment in terms of the cyclotron frequency of the electron and obtained a result which agrees with that of Taub and Kusch and is $\mu_p/\mu_o = 0.00152101 \pm 0.0013$ percent.

Hipple, Sommer, and Thomas (H15) and Bloch and Jeffries (B25) have measured the proton magnetic moment in terms of the cyclotron frequency of the proton and have obtained the values of $2.79268 \pm .00006$ and $2.79245 \pm .00020$ nuclear magnetons, respectively, when no correction is made for magnetic shielding. When the first of these is corrected with the magnetic shielding correction of Table 2, the value of the proton magnetic moment is $(2.79276 \pm .00006)$ nuclear magnetons.

Thomas, Driscoll, and Hipple (T4, T5) in their measurements of the magnetic moment of the proton in a Bureau of Standards calibrated magnetic field found $\gamma_p = 2\mu_p/\hbar = 26753.0 \pm 0.6$ sec^{-1} gauss^{-1} after Ramsey's (R14, T5, G34) correction for magnetic shielding is made.

The above experiments separately provide more or less independent calibrations of the nuclear magnetic moment scale. It is found that they all agree within the limits of error of the fundamental constants used in the evaluations. Consequently, they have been compared by DuMond (D17), Birge (B8), Purcell (P29), and others to provide even more accurate evaluations of many of the fundamental constants than heretofore available. A summary of the best values for the fundamental constants determined in this manner has been given by DuMond (D17).

B. Magnetic Shielding and Resonance Shifts

As the precision of nuclear moment measurements has increased, various small magnetic effects affecting the magnetic moment measurements have become of increasing importance. The first correction of this kind was introduced by Lamb (L1), who calculated the diamagnetic shielding by the electrons upon the nuclei of atoms. In other words, when the magnetic field H_0 is applied, the electrons are given an induced diamagnetic circulation which produces a magnetic field

$-\sigma H_0$ at the position of the nucleus which partially cancels the initially applied field, where σ is the magnetic shielding constant. Since this induced diamagnetic field is proportional to the originally applied magnetic field, it cannot be distinguished from it by varying the magnitude of the field. Instead, it has the experimental effect of making a measured nuclear moment appear slightly smaller than it actually is. Consequently, the diamagnetic shielding effect must be calculated theoretically and allowed for in inferring the magnitude of the nuclear magnetic moment from the externally applied field and the observed resonance frequency. Lamb showed that, for an atom with a spherically symmetric nuclear electrostatic field,

$$\sigma = \frac{e^2}{2mc^2} \int \frac{(x^2 + y^2)\rho}{r^3} \, d\tau = \frac{e^2}{3mc^2} \int \frac{\rho}{r} \, d\tau \tag{118}$$

where ρ is the density of electrons. This result follows almost immediately from Larmor's theorem and Ampere's law of electromagnetism. Values for this correction have been tabulated by Lamb (L1) and by Dickinson (D13), who used Hartree and Fock wave functions, respectively. Although Lamb's theory applies directly only to atoms, most measurements are made in molecules. Since no better theory was available for a long time, all corrections in molecules were made according to Lamb's theory, the correction being made only for the atom concerned.

However, it was pointed out later by Ramsey (R12, R14, R17b) that with the increased accuracy of nuclear moment measurements the error from this approximate calculation of the diamagnetic correction was important. For very light molecules, like hydrogen in particular, the error in Lamb's value of the diamagnetic correction should be comparable to the magnitude of the correction itself. Ramsey (R12, R14, R17b) showed that in molecules the magnetic shielding correction could be expressed as

$$\sigma = \frac{e^2}{3mc^2} \int \frac{\rho}{r} \, d\tau$$
$$- 2\mathrm{av} \sum_{n\lambda'} \frac{\left\{ \begin{array}{l} (0\lambda| \, \Sigma_k m_{zk}{}^0 \, |n\lambda')(n\lambda'| \, \Sigma_k m_{zk}{}^0/r_k{}^3 \, |0\lambda) \\ \quad + (0\lambda| \, \Sigma_k m_{zk}{}^0/r_k{}^3 \, |n\lambda')(n\lambda'| \, \Sigma_k m_{zk}{}^0 \, |0\lambda) \end{array} \right\}}{E_n - E_o} \tag{119}$$

where the first integral is taken over the entire molecule; the origin of

r and r_k is the nucleus for which the shielding is desired; and $(0\lambda| \Sigma_k m_{zk}{}^0 |n\lambda')$ is the matrix element between the molecular ground state and a molecular electronic excited state n, with the molecular axis in an orientation expressed by λ, of the orbital magnetic moment operator for the kth electron of $m_{zk}{}^0 = -(e\hbar/2mci)[x_k(\partial/\partial y_k) - y_k(\partial/\partial x_k)]$. The second term corresponds to the second-order paramagnetism which enters in the theory of the ordinary diamagnetic susceptibility of molecules as developed by Van Vleck (V1). Since the last term depends on the excited electronic states of the molecule, it is very difficult to evaluate. However, if $E_n - E_o$ is replaced by an average energy ΔE of the excited states, the expression can be reexpressed in a simpler form, involving only ground-state wave functions, as

$$\sigma = \frac{e^2}{3mc^2} \int \frac{\rho}{r} d\tau - \frac{4}{3\Delta E} \left(0 \left| \sum_{jk} m_j{}^0 \cdot \frac{m_k{}^0}{r_k{}^3} \right| 0 \right) \qquad (120)$$

Nevertheless, even this is very difficult to evaluate experimentally. However, Ramsey (R14, R17b, R17c, R16c) further pointed out that for linear molecules the last term in Eq. (119) is proportional to the theoretical expression developed by Brooks (B47) and Wick (W9) for the spin magnetic rotational interaction constant, i.e., for the H' of Eqs. (18) and (105). With this the diamagnetic correction constant can be expressed for a linear molecule as

$$\sigma = \frac{e^2}{3mc^2} \int \frac{\rho}{r} d\tau - \frac{\alpha^2 a_0 I}{6\mu_{NM}} \left(\Sigma_i \frac{2Z_i \mu_{NM}}{I a_i} - \frac{H'}{JM} \right) \qquad (121)$$

where a_0 is the radius of the first Bohr orbit, I the moment of inertia of the molecule, a_i the distance of the nucleus with charge Z_i from the nucleus where the shielding is desired. Where H' has been empirically measured, such as for molecular hydrogen, the second term can be directly evaluated. From this for molecular H_2 Ramsey (R14, K18) and Newell (N7a) find that $\sigma = 2.66 \times 10^{-5}$. It should be noted that Eq. (121) comes directly from Eq. (119) without the approximations involved in Eq. (120). As an alternative to the above evaluation for H_2, Hylleraas and Skavlem (H21) have evaluated, from an independently derived form of Eq. (120), the difficult term from approximate molecular hydrogen wave functions, but this calculation should be much less accurate than Ramsey's determination. Because of the difficulty of evaluating the diamagnetic correction in this manner for molecules other than hydrogen molecules, it is still customary to express the diamagnetic correction in molecules simply as the Lamb correction of the single atom containing the nucleus of interest. This procedure is fairly accurate for nuclei of large Z, since the innermost electrons of the atom are most

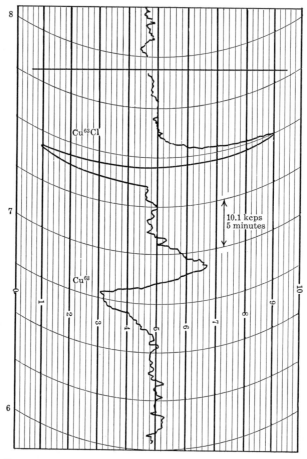

Fig. 26. Comparison of resonance frequencies of Cu^{63} in CuCl powder and in Cu metallic powder (K14).

effective in producing diamagnetic shielding due to the $1/r$ factor in Eq. (118). Thomas (T5) and Gutowsky and McClure (G34) have recently measured the ratios of the apparent magnetic moments of the proton in H_2, mineral oil, and H_2O. When these measurements are combined with Ramsey's (R14) value for H_2, the magnetic shielding for mineral oil and H_2O can be computed directly. The results are that the shielding factors σ for H_2, mineral oil, and H_2O are 2.66×10^{-5}, 2.82×10^{-5}, and 2.60×10^{-5} respectively. Ramsey and Purcell (R16b) have recently estimated the effect of electron shielding on the nuclear spin-spin magnetic interaction of Eq. (105) and have shown that the electron spin magnetic moments make a particularly important contribution to the shielding in this case even though they do not enter in the shielding by an external field as in Eq. (119).

An interesting magnetic effect has been discovered by Knight (K14). He finds that the resonance frequencies of sodium, aluminum, copper, and other metals are several tenths of a percent higher when the nuclei are in a metallic state than when they are in the form of either powdered or dissolved salts. Townes (K14, T29, K17a) has suggested that this effect is probably due to the paramagnetism of the conduction electrons in the metal when they are in the immediate vicinity of the nucleus. This shift in resonance frequency is illustrated in Fig. 26. The Knight shift is discussed in much greater detail in Section 5I.

A different magnetic shift has been discovered by Dickinson (B27). In many nuclear resonance experiments paramagnetic ions are added to the liquid sample to reduce the relaxation time, and it was originally assumed that, owing to the spherically symmetric nature of the problem, the paramagnetic ions would not shift the resonance frequency. However, Dickinson (B27) has empirically found that such ions do shift the resonance frequency and that the magnitude of the shift is proportional to the ion concentration. The resonance frequency can be either increased or decreased by the presence of the ions. For the fluorine resonance in SbF_3 and for 10^{21} Fe^{++} ions per cubic centimeter the shift is 0.007 percent as shown in Fig. 27. Bloembergen and Dickinson (B27) have attributed this result to the effect of the electric field of the ion concerned upon the magnetic moment of the paramagnetic ion. From simple crystal studies it is known that this effect of the electric field upon the magnetic moment depends on the relative orientation between the electric and the magnetic fields, as discussed in Section 5R. Therefore this change in magnetic moment of the paramagnetic ion will not occur symmetrically about the nucleus of interest, and consequently a resultant magnetic field can be produced which gives rise to the observed shift.

A magnetic shift different from the two immediately preceding ones has been discovered by Knight (K14), Dickinson (D12), and Proctor and Yu (P24). These observers have independently found a shift of resonance frequency of the same nucleus in different chemical compounds. This shift is sometimes called the chemical effect. For example, there are shifts of 0.015 and of 0.05 percent in different compounds

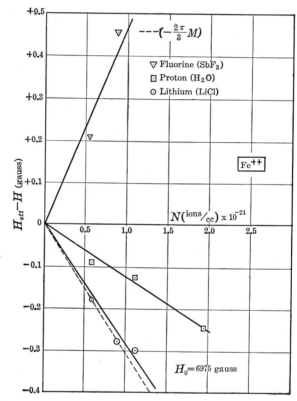

Fig. 27. The shift of the magnetic resonance of F^{19}, H^1, and Li^7 in aqueous solutions containing various amounts of $FeCl_2$. The samples have the shape of a long cylinder with the axis perpendicular to H_0. The dotted line represents the result to be expected if there were no contribution to the local field at the nucleus from the paramagnetic ions inside a small sphere surrounding the nucleus (B27).

of nitrogen. Ramsey (R12, R14) and Proctor and Yu (P24) have attributed this shift to the changes in different molecular compounds of both terms of the magnetic shielding expression (119). Lindström (L8), Thomas (T5), and Gutowsky and McClure (G34) have found shifts of the order of a few parts in a million for hydrogen in water, mineral oil, and H_2, as expected from Ramsey's (R14) theory.

In view of the above magnetic shifts and diamagnetic corrections, it is important that reports on future high-precision measurements of nuclear moments should include a precise statement of the conditions of the experiment and the nature of the diamagnetic corrections made.

Another discrepancy exists in the measurements of the magnetic moments of gallium in gallium chloride and in atomic gallium. If the atomic gallium measurements depended simply on the hyperfine structure separation, the discrepancy would be expected because of the difficulty in calculating the factors in the interaction constant a of Section 2. However, the atomic measurements were made through the term of Eq. (36) depending on the direct interaction of the nuclear moment and the external field and hence do not depend on the theory of $\Delta\nu$. The magnitude of the discrepancy can be seen from the following numerical values: Pound (P14) and Bitter (B10) find

$$\frac{\mu\,(Ga^{71})}{\mu\,(H^1)} = 0.9148 \pm 0.0004 \qquad \frac{\mu\,(Ga^{69})}{\mu\,(H^1)} = 0.7203 \pm 0.0005$$

and Becker and Kusch (B5, K47) find, with atomic gallium,

$$\frac{\mu\,(Ga^{71})}{\mu\,(H^1)} = 0.9078 \pm 0.0015 \qquad \frac{\mu\,(Ga^{69})}{\mu\,(H^1)} = 0.7146 \pm 0.0015$$

All the preceding figures contain no diamagnetic corrections. The discrepancy has recently been explained by Foley (F12) as due to the mixing of the $^2P_{1/2}$ and $^2P_{3/2}$ states of the atom by the external magnetic field.

C. Nuclear Moment Tables

The values obtained for the nuclear moments by the above methods are given in Table 1. All the magnetic moment values are based on the hypothesis that the magnetic moment of the proton is assumed to be exactly 2.79255, the most probable value at the time the table was prepared. The diamagnetic corrections used for these data are those listed in Table 2. Table 3 lists magnetic moment ratios and quadrupole moment ratios for pairs of isotopes in certain cases where the ratios are known much more accurately than is either quantity by itself. Table 4 lists the hyperfine structure separation $\Delta\nu$ of certain nuclei for which this has been accurately measured. Extensive use has been made of the tables of Poss (P10) and Mack (M3) in the preparation of these tables.

TABLE 1

Nuclear Moments

The quantities and units of this table are defined as in the text. The asterisk (*) after a mass number indicates a radioactive isotope. Spin values listed in parentheses either are in doubt or are inferred only from theoretical arguments in the absence of experimental evidence. All magnetic moment values are relative to an assumed value for the magnetic moment of the proton of exactly 2.79255 nuclear magnetons. This was the best value at the time the table was prepared. As this volume goes to press the best value is 2.79276, so for the highest accuracy the moments listed should be multiplied by 2.79276/2.79255. As the listed experimental errors also include no allowance for the error in the fundamental proton moment calibration, to obtain the error in the absolute determination of any magnetic moment one must increase the listed error to allow for the 0.0029 percent error in the proton moment value. Quantities following the ± express the uncertainty, on the above basis, of the last printed numeral of the preceding listed value. These uncertainties do not include all systematic errors such as those from the use of incorrect magnetic shielding constants. The magnetic shielding constants assumed and the magnitude of the moment shifts made in obtaining the values below are listed in Table 2. Almost all the values of Q are subject to a large uncertainty due to lack of knowledge of $\partial^2 V^e/\partial z^2$; for those cases in which the value of $\partial^2 V^e/\partial z^2$ is particularly uncertain the value of Q is enclosed in parentheses. All the references relate to the reference list on pages 142 to 159; in this list the method of observation and the substance studied are indicated. The present best value of the nuclear magneton is $(5.04929 \pm 0.00020) \times 10^{-24}$ erg·gauss^{-1} (D17). In most cases, data published after January 1, 1952, are not included in this table. Values marked with a dagger (†) were added in proof and were not adjusted to a consistent set of shielding constants or absolute values. Only moments of nuclear ground states are given in this table. For excited states and for data published after 1952, see the most recent review articles (ZF6, ZW1a).

Z	Atom	A	I	μ (nuclear magnetons)	Q $(10^{-24}$ cm$^2)$	References		
						I	μ	Q
0	n	1 *	$\frac{1}{2}$	-1.91280 ± 9		S36, H7a	A1, A8, B24, R31	
1	H	1	$\frac{1}{2}$	$+2.79255 \pm 0$		D9, H12, K9, K18	K9, M22, T4, T1, R31, G2, H15, J8, T5, K18	
		2	1	$+0.857348 \pm 3$	$+0.002738 \pm 16$	F2, M34	K9, A8, R28, B23, B9, W11, S41, Z5, S44, L5, L8, K18	K8, N11, N6, N7, F3, C7, H7, K18
		3 *	$\frac{1}{2}$	$+2.978635 \pm 28$		B21, D14	A4, B22	
2	He	3	$\frac{1}{2}$	$(-)2.127414 \pm 3$		D15	A5	
		4	0			M27		

TABLE 1 (*Continued*)

NUCLEAR MOMENTS

Z	Atom	A	I	μ (nuclear magnetons)	Q (10^{-24} cm^2)	References		
						I	μ	Q
3	Li	6	1	$+0.82189 \pm 4$	0.0005 ± 5	M6	K44, K46	K43
		7	$\frac{3}{2}$	$+3.25586 \pm 11$	$+(0.02) \pm 2$	H10, G25, G29	G26, F16, M22, B10, K44, Z5	K43
4	Be	9	$\frac{3}{2}$	-1.1774 ± 8		H10a	K37, D10, C9, A1a, S39, Z6	
5	B	10	3	$+1.8004 \pm 7$	$+0.06 \pm 4$	G10, W4, G12	M19, B10	G10, G12
		11	$\frac{3}{2}$	$+2.68858 \pm 28$	$+0.03 \pm 2$	G10	M19, B10, A2, Z5, A3, S39	C10
6	C	12	0			M27, H12		
		13	$\frac{1}{2}$	$+0.70225 \pm 14$		T21, H11, J14, T24	H11, P11	
		14 *	0			J14, R29		
7	N	14	1	$+0.40365 \pm 3$	$+0.02$	K35, O4, R20, T23	K38, P22, P23	D1, T23, T25, S39a
		15	$\frac{1}{2}$	-0.28299 ± 3		K36, W13	Z1, P22, P23	
		16	2					
8	O	16	0			M27		
		17	$\frac{5}{2}$	-1.8928 ± 2 †	-0.005 ± 2	A1a, G4a	A1a	L11, G4a
		18	0		$\|<4 \cdot 10^{-3}\|$	M14b		T31
9	F	19	$\frac{1}{2}$	$+2.6285 \pm 7$		G1, G9	C2, M22, P11, S41, Z5	
10	Ne	20	(0)	~ 0			H8	
		21	$\frac{3}{2}$ $(>\frac{3}{2}?)$	<0		K16	K16	
		22	(0)	~ 0			H8	
11	Na	22 *	3	$+1.74582 \pm 30$		D3	D6	
		23	$\frac{3}{2}$	$+2.21711 \pm 25$	$\neq 0$	J15, G27, R1	E1, F16, M22, B10, K44, Z5, S39	N9
		24 *	4			S45b		
12	Mg	24	(0)	~ 0			M28	
		25	$(\frac{5}{2})$	-0.85466 ± 15 †		C21, C24, K12	A1a	
		26	(0)	~ 0			A13	
13	Al	27	$\frac{5}{2}$	$+3.6408 \pm 4$	$+0.156 \pm 3$	H14, L7, H10a	M20, B10, Z5, S39	L6, D7, L7
14	Si	28	(0)		~ 0			T27
		29	$\frac{1}{2}$	-0.55492 ± 4 †	~ 0	H10a	H10a	T27
		30	(0)		~ 0			T27

TABLE 1 (*Continued*)

NUCLEAR MOMENTS

Z	Atom	A	I	μ (nuclear magnetons)	Q (10^{-24} cm^2)	References I	References μ	References Q
15	P	31	$\frac{1}{2}$	$+1.13165 \pm 20$		J13	P14, B10, C9, C23, S39	
16	S	32	0			N5, O3		
		33	$\frac{3}{2}$	$+0.64292 \pm 14$ †	-0.08	T25	J12, R30, X1, J11, D9a	T25
		34	(0)		$\lvert <2\cdot10^{-3}\rvert$			T24, T25
		35 *	$\frac{3}{2}$		$+0.06$	C13, C14		T25, C13, C14
		36	(0)		<0.01			L11
17	Cl	35	$\frac{3}{2}$	$+0.82191 \pm 22$	-0.07894 ± 2 †	T23	B10, D7, C9	T25, G9, D4, D7, L4, D8, G4a, S45a, J1
		36 *	2		-0.0172 ± 4	T26, J15a		T26, J15a
		37	$\frac{3}{2}$	$+0.68414 \pm 24$	-0.06213 ± 2 †	T23	K39, D7, P22, P23	T25, G9, D4, D7, Z4, D8, G4a, S45a, J1
18	A		(0)	~0			K28	
19	K	39	$\frac{3}{2}$	$+0.391 \pm 1$		M15, K38	M1, F16, K38, K40, T1	
		40 *	4	-1.291 ± 4		Z2	Z2, T1, D6	
		41	$\frac{3}{2}$	$+0.215 \pm 1$		M15, M5	M15, M5, K44, T1	
20	Ca	40	(0)	~0			F20	
		43						
21	Sc	45	$\frac{7}{2}$	$+4.7556 \pm 10$		K26, S21	K27, P25, H20, S39, R14a	
22	Ti	47						
		49						
23	V	51	$\frac{7}{2}$	$+5.1478 \pm 5$		K25, P22, S39, B14b	K15, P22, Z6	
24	Cr	53	$\frac{3}{2}$	$(-)0.45$		Z6	Z6	
25	Mn	55	$\frac{5}{2}$	$+3.4677 \pm 4$		W6, B14c	W6, F10, P22, C10, P23, A13a, S39	

TABLE 1 (*Continued*)

NUCLEAR MOMENTS

Z	Atom	A	I	μ (nuclear magnetons)	Q $(10^{-24}$ cm$^2)$	References I	μ	Q
26	Fe	57		~0			G31, B48, R34	
27	Co	59	$\frac{7}{2}$	+4.6482		G22, K25, M24, R22	M24, P22, P23	
28	Ni	61		~0			A13	
29	Cu	63	$\frac{3}{2}$	+2.22617 ± 36	−0.13 ± 1	R25	G21, S28, S32, P13, B10, Z5, A13a, S39	S24, S28, B45, Z6
		65	$\frac{3}{2}$	+2.3845 ± 4	−0.12 ± 1	R25	G21, S28, S32, P13, B10, Z5, A13a, S39	S24, S28, B45, Z6
30	Zn	64	(0)	~0			M28	
		66	(0)	~0			M28	
		67	$\frac{5}{2}$	+0.9		L14, A9	L14	
		68	(0)	~0			M28	
31	Ga	69	$\frac{3}{2}$	+2.0167 ± 11	+0.2318 ± 23	J2, C1	G21, S30, B5, P14	S30, B5, D7
		71	$\frac{3}{2}$	+2.5614 ± 10	+0.1461 ± 15	J2, C1	G21, S30, B5, P14	S30, B5, D7
32	Ge	70	(0)		$\lvert <7\cdot10^{-3}\rvert$			T27
		72	(0)		$\lvert <7\cdot10^{-3}\rvert$			T27
		73	$\frac{9}{2}$		−0.21 ± 10	T27		T27
		74	(0)		$\lvert <7\cdot10^{-3}\rvert$			T27
		76	(0)		$\lvert <7\cdot10^{-3}\rvert$			T27
33	As	75	$\frac{3}{2}$	+1.4347 ± 3 †	+0.3 ± 2	T8, R18, C17, D2	G21, S24, S29, M33, D9a	S24, S29, D2
34	Se	74	(0)			S47		
		76	(0)	~0	$\lvert <2\cdot10^{-3}\rvert$	S47	R9	S45, T30
		77	$\frac{1}{2}$		$\lvert <2\cdot10^{-3}\rvert$	S47, M1		S40, G13, T30, Z6
		78	(0)	~0	$\lvert <2\cdot10^{-3}\rvert$	S47	R9	S47, T30
		80	0		$\lvert <2\cdot10^{-3}\rvert$	S47		S47, T30
		82	(0)	~0			R9	
35	Br	79	$\frac{3}{2}$	+2.10576 ± 37	+0.26 ± 8	B49, T7, T23	C2, B46, P12, Z5, S39	T14, G8, G9, T25, P12
		81	$\frac{3}{2}$	+2.2696 ± 5	+0.21 ± 7	B49, T7, T23	C2, B46, P12, B10, Z5, S39	T14, G8, G9, T25, P12

TABLE 1 (*Continued*)

NUCLEAR MOMENTS

Z	Atom	A	I	μ (nuclear magnetons)	Q (10^{-24} cm^2)	References		
						I	μ	Q
36	Kr	82	(0)	~ 0			K22	
		83	$\frac{9}{2}$	-0.9704	$+0.15$	M29, K34, K16	K22, S33, K10	K34, S33
		84	(0)	~ 0			K22	
		86	(0)	~ 0			K22	
37	Rb	85	$\frac{5}{2}$	$+1.3532 \pm 4$			K21, K39, B10, K44, C9, Y1, S39	
		86 *	2	-1.68 ± 40		B4b	B4b	
		87	$\frac{3}{2}$	$+2.7501 \pm 5$		K21, M16	K21, K38, B10, Z5, Y1, S39	
38	Sr	86	(0)				F20	
		87	$\frac{9}{2}$	-1.1		H13	H13	
		88	(0)	~ 0			F20	
39	Y	89	$\frac{1}{2}$	-0.14		W12, C22, K36a	W12, C22, K36a	
40	Zr	91	$\frac{5}{2}$			A10		
41	Nb	93	$\frac{9}{2}$	$+6.165 \pm 32$	~ 0	B3	M12, C10, S38, S35	M12
42	Mo	92	(0)	~ 0			A13	
		94	(0)	~ 0			A13	
		95	$(\frac{5}{2})$	-0.9140 ± 2 †			A13, Z6	
		96	(0)	~ 0			A13	
		97	$(\frac{5}{2})$	-0.9332 ± 1 †			A13, Z6	
		98	(0)	~ 0			A13	
		100	(0)	~ 0			A13	
43	Tc	99 *	$\frac{9}{2}$	$+5.3 \pm 5$		K12a	Z6	
44	Ru	99						
		101						
45	Rh	103	$\frac{1}{2}$	-0.11		S40, K36a	S40, K36a	
46	Pd	105	$(\frac{5}{2})$	(-0.6)		Z6	Z6	
		111 *	$\frac{1}{2}$			M12a		
47	Ag	107	$\frac{1}{2}$	-0.111 ± 8		J6	J6, C19, K33a, Z6	
		109	$\frac{1}{2}$	-0.129 ± 8		J6	J6, C19, K33a, Z6	
		111 *	$\frac{1}{2}$			M12a		
48	Cd	110	(0)	~ 0			S13	
		111	$\frac{1}{2}$	-0.59492 ± 8		S13, M12a	G21, J16, P21, P22, P26	
		112	(0)	~ 0				

TABLE 1 *(Continued)*

NUCLEAR MOMENTS

Z	Atom	A	I	μ (nuclear magnetons)	Q $(10^{-24}\ cm^2)$	References		
						I	μ	Q
48	Cd	113	$\frac{1}{2}$	-0.62238 ± 8		S13	G21, J16, P21, P22, P26	
		114	(0)	~ 0			S13	
		116	(0)	~ 0			S13	
49	In	111 *	$\frac{9}{2}$			M12a		
		113	$\frac{9}{2}$	$+5.486 \pm 3$	1.144	J3, B1, H9	H9, T1	M7
		114 *	1			S45c		
		115 *	$\frac{9}{2}$	$+5.500 \pm 3$	1.161	C1, J3, P2	S31, M17, K42, T1, M7	S24, B1, H5, D7, M7
50	Sn	111 *	$\frac{7}{2}$			M12a		
		115	$\frac{1}{2}$	-0.9177 ± 2		G30	G30, P21, P22, P26	
		116	(0)	~ 0			M28	
		117	$\frac{1}{2}$	-0.9997 ± 2		S17, T9	T9, T15, P20, P22, P26	
		118	(0)	~ 0			M28	
		119	$\frac{1}{2}$	-1.0459 ± 2		S17, T9	T9, T15, P20, P22, P26	
		120	(0)	~ 0			M28	
51	Sb	121	$\frac{5}{2}$	$+3.3591 \pm 5$	-0.3 ± 2	B2, C18	G21, C18, P25, C15	S24, T17, M32
		123	$\frac{7}{2}$	$+2.5465 \pm 5$	-1.2 ± 2	B2, C18	G21, C18, P25, C15	S24, T17, M32
52	Te	123	$\frac{1}{2}$	-0.73188 ± 4 †		M2, F15	M2, R34, D9a	
		125	$\frac{1}{2}$	-0.88235 ± 4 †		F14, F15	R34, D9a	
		126	(0)	~ 0			R9	
		128	(0)	~ 0			R9	
		130	(0)	~ 0			R9	
53	I	127	$\frac{5}{2}$	$+2.8086 \pm 8$	-0.59 ± 20	M30, G8	P13, Z5	S10, M31, G8, G9, T25, W2a, Y1, S39
		129 *	$\frac{7}{2}$	$+2.6173 \pm 3$ †	-0.43 ± 15	L9	G9	L9, W2a
54	Xe	129	$\frac{1}{2}$	-0.7766 ± 1		K23, J17, R23, K17	K22, P25	
		131	$\frac{3}{2}$	$+0.70$	$\|<0\cdot1\|$	K23, K34, R23, K17	K22, Z6	K34, S33
		132	(0)	~ 0			J17	
		134	(0)	~ 0			J17	
		136	(0)	~ 0			J17	
55	Cs	133	$\frac{7}{2}$	$+2.5771 \pm 9$	$\|\leq 0\cdot3\|$	K20, J4, C11, F13	C11, K38, B10, D6, C9, S39	S11
		134 *	4	4.1 ± 4		F21a	F21a	

TABLE 1 *(Continued)*

NUCLEAR MOMENTS

Z	Atom	A	I	μ (nuclear magnetons)	Q $(10^{-24}\,cm^2)$	References I	References μ	References Q
55	Cs	135 *	7/2	+2.7271 ± 33		N4	N4, D6	
		137 *	7/2	+2.8397 ± 30		D5, N4	N4, D6	
56	Ba	134	(0)	~0			A13	
		135	3/2	+0.8346 ± 25		M29, H11, A11	H11	
		136	(0)	~0			A13	
		137	3/2	+0.9351 ± 27		K2, M29, H11, A11	H11	
		138	(0)	~0			A13	
57	La	139	7/2	+2.7760 ± 28	≠0	W7, A6	W12, D11, C9, S39	D11
59	Pr	141	5/2			W5	C10	
60	Nd	143	7/2	−1.0 ± 2		M33, B14b	M33, Z6	
		145	7/2	−0.65 ± 9		M33, B14b	M33, Z6	
62	Sm	147	5/2	−0.30 ± 5		B44, M33	M33	
		149	5/2	−0.25 ± 4		B44, M33	M33	
63	Eu	151	5/2	+3.4	+1.2	S24	S24	S24
		153	5/2	+1.5	+2.5	S24	S24	S24
64	Gd	155						
		157						
65	Tb	159	3/2			S19		
66	Dy	161						
		163						
67	Ho	165	7/2			S23		
68	Er	167	7/2			B14b		
69	Tm	169	1/2			S22		
70	Yb	171	1/2	+0.45		S33	S33	
		173	5/2	−0.65	+3.9 ± 4	S33	S33	S33
71	Lu	175	7/2	+2.6	+5.9	S19	S24, G6	S25, S24, C5, G6
		176 *	≥7	+3.8	+7 ± 1	S34	S34	S34
72	Hf	177	(1/2, 3/2)			R21		
		178	(0)	~0			R21	
		179	(1/2, 3/2)			R21		
		180	(0)	~0			R21	
73	Ta	181	7/2	+2.1	+6	G23, G5	G5	S12

TABLE 1 (*Continued*)

NUCLEAR MOMENTS

Z	Atom	A	I	μ (nuclear magnetons)	Q $(10^{-24}\ cm^2)$	References		
						I	μ	Q
74	W	182	(0)				G24	
		183	$\frac{1}{2}$			G24, K30, F15		
		184	(0)				G24	
		186	(0)				G24	
75	Re	185	$\frac{5}{2}$	$+3.1433 \pm 6$ †	$(+2.8)$	G28, M13, Z3	S32, S9, A1a	S32
		187	$\frac{5}{2}$	$+3.1755 \pm 6$ †	$+2.6$	G28, M13, Z3	S32, S9, A1a	S32
76	Os	187						
		189	$\frac{1}{2}$	$+0.6 \pm 1$		K6	S47b	
77	Ir	191	$\frac{3}{2}$			V4, M33, B44	V4, M33	
		193	$\frac{3}{2}$			V4, M33, B44	V4, M33	
78	Pt	194	(0)	~ 0			F23	
		195	$\frac{1}{2}$	$+0.60592 \pm 8$		T12	S7, P21, P22	
		196	(0)	~ 0			F23	
79	Au	197	$\frac{3}{2}$	$+0.20$		E2	E2	
80	Hg	198	(0)	~ 0			T6	
		199	$\frac{1}{2}$	$+0.50413 \pm 13$		S15	G21, S26, M26, P21, P22	
		200	(0)	~ 0			T6	
		201	$\frac{3}{2}$	-0.5590 ± 1	$+0.5$	S15	G21, S26, M26	S24, S26
		202	(0)	~ 0			T6	
		204	(0)	~ 0			T6	
81	Tl	203	$\frac{1}{2}$	$+1.6114 \pm 3$		S13, S14, S39	G21, S31, S32, P26, P18, P11, C20	
		205	$\frac{1}{2}$	$+1.6272 \pm 3$		S13, S14, S39	G21, S31, S32, P26, P18, P11, C20	
82	Pb	204	(0)	~ 0			G3	
		206	(0)	~ 0			M28	
		207	$\frac{1}{2}$	$+0.5894 \pm 1$		K19, C25	G21, C25, P20, C20, S5, P26	
		208	(0)	~ 0			M28	
83	Bi	209	$\frac{9}{2}$	$+4.0801 \pm 5$	-0.4	G16	G21, W12, X1, P25, K12	S27
89	Ac	227 *	$\frac{3}{2}$			T18		
91	Pa	231 *	$\frac{3}{2}$			S18		
92	U	235 *	$(\frac{5}{2}, \frac{7}{2})$			A7, T16, S47a		
93	Np	237 *	$\frac{5}{2}$			T18		

TABLE 2

Magnetic Shielding Corrections

This table lists the magnetic shielding corrections assumed in the computation of Table 1. The second column is the value of $1 - \sigma$ (σ is defined in Section 4B). The fourth and eighth columns list the correction in nuclear magnetons that has been added to the nuclear moment to provide the data of Table 1. In so far as the dependence of the shielding on the chemical compound can be neglected, the frequency ratio that should be experimentally observed for two nuclei can be obtained by calculating the frequency ratio for the moments resulting after the corrections below are subtracted from the magnetic moment values in Table 1 of each of the nuclei concerned. All shielding constants σ below are based on Lamb's (L1) Hartree function calculations except for hydrogen, where Ramsey's (R14) and Newell's (N7a) value of 0.0000266 is used for H_2 and where the combination of the results of Ramsey (R14), Thomas (T5), and Gutowsky and McClure (G34) leads to values of σ for mineral oil and H_2O of 0.0000282 and 0.0000260 respectively.

Z	$1 - \sigma$	A	Added Correction (nuclear magnetons)	Z	$1 - \sigma$	A	Added Correction (nuclear magnetons)
0	0	1	0	7	0.999744	14	0.00010
						15	0.00007
1 †	0.9999734	1	0.000076				
		2	0.000023	9	0.999611	19	0.0010
		3	0.000079				
				11	0.999456	22	0.00095
1 ‡	0.9999718	1	0.000081			23	0.00121
		2	0.000024				
		3	0.000084	13	0.999282	27	0.00261
1 §	0.9999740	1	0.000074	15	0.999088	31	0.00103
		2	0.000022				
		3	0.000077	17	0.998877	35	0.00092
						37	0.00077
2	0.999930	3	0.000149				
				19	0.998687	39	0.0005
3	0.9999192	6	0.00007			40	0.0017
		7	0.00026			41	0.0003
4	0.9998785	9	0.000143	21	0.998490	45	0.0072
5	0.999832	10	0.00030	23	0.998293	51	0.0088
		11	0.00045				
				25	0.998083	55	0.0066
6	0.999802	13	0.00014				

† H_2.   ‡ Mineral oil.   § H_2O.

TABLE 2 (*Continued*)

MAGNETIC SHIELDING CORRECTIONS

Z	$1 - \sigma$	A	Added Correction (nuclear magnetons)	Z	$1 - \sigma$	A	Added Correction (nuclear magnetons)
27	0.997858	59	0.0100	51	0.994763	121	0.0176
						123	0.0133
29	0.997612	63	0.00532				
		65	0.00569	53	0.994553	127	0.00530
						129	0.0149
31	0.997387	69	0.0053	54	0.994411	129	0.0043
		71	0.0067				
35	0.996916	79	0.0065	55	0.994269	133	0.0148
	°	81	0.0070			135	0.0156
						137	0.0163
36	0.996800	83	0.0031				
				56	0.994125	135	0.0049
37	0.996671	85	0.00450			137	0.0055
		87	0.00915				
				57	0.993983	139	0.01672
47	0.99538	107	0.0004	78	0.990702	195	0.00563
		109	0.0008				
48	0.995248	111	0.00283	79	0.990526	197	0.0019
		113	0.00296				
				80	0.990349	199	0.00486
49	0.995110	113	0.0268	81	0.990170	203	0.01584
		115	0.0269			205	0.01600
50	0.994973	115	0.00461	82	0.989989	207	0.00590
		117	0.00502				
		119	0.00526	83	0.989808	209	0.0416

TABLE 3

Nuclear Moment Ratios

In certain cases the ratios of two nuclear moments are known to a much greater accuracy than is either of the moments alone. Such cases are listed in this table. If (hfs) is written after a magnetic moment ratio, it was determined from the ratio of the atomic hyperfine structure splitting; otherwise it is from the frequency ratio of the resonances in an external magnetic field. The number following the $\pm$ indicates the uncertainty in the last printed numeral of the preceding listed value. Data published after January 1, 1951, are not included in this table.

Ratio	μ Ratio	Q Ratio	References
$_1\mathrm{H}^2/_1\mathrm{H}^1$	0.3070125 ± 30		K9, A8, R28, B23, B9, W11, S41, Z5, S44, L5
$_1\mathrm{H}^3/_1\mathrm{H}^1$	1.066636 ± 10		A4, B22
$_3\mathrm{Li}^7/_3\mathrm{Li}^6$	3.96141 ± 8	44 ± 4	K46, K43
	3.96092 ± 8 (hfs)		K46, K44, K40
$_5\mathrm{B}^{11}/_5\mathrm{B}^{10}$	1.4931 ± 4	0.47 ± 4	B10, G10
$_{16}\mathrm{S}^{35}/_{16}\mathrm{S}^{33}$		-0.70 ± 16	C13, T25
$_{17}\mathrm{Cl}^{36}/_{17}\mathrm{Cl}^{35}$		0.271 ± 5	T26, D7
$_{17}\mathrm{Cl}^{35}/_{17}\mathrm{Cl}^{37}$	1.2013 ± 1	1.26878 ± 15	D7, G8, T25, Z4, P23, D8, G4a, L9a
	1.20136 ± 5	1.2686 ± 4	D7, J1
$_{29}\mathrm{Cu}^{65}/_{29}\mathrm{Cu}^{63}$	1.0711 ± 2	0.922 ± 7	B10, P13, Z5, B4a, B14a
$_{31}\mathrm{Ga}^{71}/_{31}\mathrm{Ga}^{69}$	1.2701 ± 4	0.6302 ± 2	P14, S30
	1.2706 ± 1 (hfs)		B5
$_{35}\mathrm{Br}^{81}/_{35}\mathrm{Br}^{79}$	1.0779 ± 3	0.835	B46, P12, Z5, G8, T25
$_{37}\mathrm{Rb}^{87}/_{37}\mathrm{Rb}^{85}$	2.0327 ± 10		B10, Z5, C9, K39
	2.0261 ± 3 (hfs)		M21
$_{48}\mathrm{Cd}^{113}/_{48}\mathrm{Cd}^{111}$	1.0461 ± 1		P26
$_{49}\mathrm{In}^{115}/_{49}\mathrm{In}^{113}$	1.0022 ± 1	1.0146	H9, M7
$_{50}\mathrm{Sn}^{117}/_{50}\mathrm{Sn}^{115}$	1.0894 ± 1		P26
$_{50}\mathrm{Sn}^{119}/_{50}\mathrm{Sn}^{117}$	1.0465 ± 1		P20, P26
$_{51}\mathrm{Sb}^{123}/_{51}\mathrm{Sb}^{121}$	0.760		T17
$_{52}\mathrm{Te}^{125}/_{52}\mathrm{Te}^{123}$	1.208		M2
$_{53}\mathrm{I}^{129}/_{53}\mathrm{I}^{127}$	0.9318	0.7353	G9, L9, W2a
$_{54}\mathrm{Xe}^{131}/_{54}\mathrm{Xe}^{129}$	-0.90		K22
$_{55}\mathrm{Cs}^{135}/_{55}\mathrm{Cs}^{133}$	1.0578 ± 9		D6
$_{55}\mathrm{Cs}^{137}/_{55}\mathrm{Cs}^{133}$	1.1016 ± 8		D6
$_{56}\mathrm{Ba}^{137}/_{56}\mathrm{Ba}^{135}$	1.1174 ± 10		H11
$_{63}\mathrm{Eu}^{153}/_{63}\mathrm{Eu}^{151}$	2.24		S24, S9
$_{75}\mathrm{Re}^{187}/_{75}\mathrm{Re}^{185}$	1.01026 ± 8		S32, A1a
$_{77}\mathrm{Ir}^{193}/_{77}\mathrm{Ir}^{191}$	-1.109		V4
$_{80}\mathrm{Hg}^{201}/_{80}\mathrm{Hg}^{199}$	-1.1089		S26
$_{81}\mathrm{Tl}^{205}/_{81}\mathrm{Tl}^{203}$	1.00986 ± 5		S32, P11, P19, P26
	1.00947 ± 20 (hfs)		B7

TABLE 4

HYPERFINE STRUCTURE SEPARATIONS

This table lists certain cases for which there are very accurate data on atomic hyperfine structure separation in ground states of atoms with an electronic angular momentum of $\frac{1}{2}$. The number following the $\pm$ indicates the uncertainty in the last printed numeral of the preceding listed value. The figure below can be converted into cm^{-1} by multiplication by $10^6/c = 3.33569 \times 10^{-5}\,cm^{-1}\,Mc^{-1} \pm 0.0003$ percent. Data published after January 1, 1951, are not included in this table. The asterisk (*) after a mass number indicates a radioactive isotope.

Z	Atom	A	$\Delta\nu$ (Mc sec^{-1})	References
1	H	1	1420.4051 ± 3	N1, N2, N3
	D	2	327.38424 ± 14	N1, N2, N3
	T	3	1516.702 ± 10	N2, A2a
3	Li	6	228.208 ± 5	K44, K40
		7	803.512 ± 15	K44, K40
11	Na	22 *	1220.64 ± 4	D6
		23	1771.61 ± 3	K44, M21
13	Al	27	1450 ± 30	L7, J6
19	K	39	461.723 ± 10	K44, K40
		40 *	1285.73 ± 5	D6, Z2
		41	254.02 ± 2	
31	Ga	69	2677.56 ± 10	B5, R24
		71	3402.09 ± 20	B5, R24
37	Rb	85	3035.7 ± 2	K44, M21
		87	6834.1 ± 10	K44, M21
49	In	113	11387 ± 4	H9, H5
		115	11413 ± 3	H9, H5
55	Cs	133	9192.76 ± 10	K44, M21
		135 *	9724 ± 8	D6
		137 *	10126 ± 7	D6
81	Tl	203	21113 ± 3	B7
		205	21312 ± 3	B7

D. Significance of Some Nuclear Moment Results

Although there are many ways in which the measured values of the nuclear moments and statistics are important, the following results are of particular significance.

(1) A nucleus whose mass number is odd satisfies Fermi-Dirac statistics, and a nucleus whose mass number is even satisfies Bose-Einstein statistics. This is reasonable since the proton and neutron each separately satisfies Fermi-Dirac statistics, whence interchanging two identical nuclei each of which has n such nucleons will multiply the wave function by $(-1)^n$ as can be seen by interchanging the nucleons one at a time. Hence, if n is even, there is no change in the sign of the wave function, whereas it is reversed if n is odd.

(2) The nuclear spin is half-integral if the mass number is odd and integral if the mass number is even. A combination of this result with the preceding one implies that Fermi-Dirac statistics is associated with half-integral spins while Bose-Einstein statistics and even spins are associated. Pauli (P6) from general field theory considerations has shown that this association must occur for all elementary particles. Pauli's theorem is reasonable since a particle with spin $\frac{1}{2}$ requires a Dirac type of equation with negative energy states and only with Fermi-Dirac statistics can these negative energy states be filled and other particles excluded from them.

(3) The proton moment is not exactly one nuclear magneton and the neutron moment is not exactly zero, as would be expected from the simplest considerations based on Dirac's electron theory. It is, however, always possible to add an additional magnetic moment (P5) to the one that naturally arises in Dirac's theory. Attempts have been made (F22, P7, S43, K3, L13, C3, D16, B31, L10) with partial success to account for this on the basis of the meson field theory of nuclear forces, since the resultant magnetic moment is contributed to by the magnetic moment and currents of the mesons which have a finite probability of existence within the range of nuclear forces of the heavy particle.

(4) The existence of the quadrupole moment of the deuteron indicates that the ground state of the deuteron is not spherically symmetrical as had been expected on the basis of the theories in existence prior to the time of the first discovery of the deuteron's quadrupole moment by Kellogg, Rabi, Ramsey, and Zacharias (K8). Rarita and Schwinger (R19) were able to account for the spherical asymmetry by introducing an additional non-central spin-dependent force, or so-called

tensor force, which makes the ground state of the deuteron a mixture of a ^3S and ^3D state.

(5) The magnetic moment of the proton plus that of the neutron is close to the moment of the deuteron, but not exactly so since it is too high by 0.0225 ± 0.003 nuclear magnetons. Hence the nuclear moments are nearly but not exactly additive. That there should be a departure was predicted by Rarita and Schwinger (R19) on the basis of their theory of the deuteron quadrupole moment. In fact, they predicted the observed departure from additivity with a surprising accuracy, which may be in part accidental because of several approximations involved in the theory. Analyses of this problem, including discussion of the approximations involved and in particular relativistic effects, have been given by Sachs (S3), Breit (B39), and Primakoff (P18).

(6) The magnetic moments of $_1H^3$ and $_2He^3$ are not exactly the same as the moments of the proton and neutron as would be the case with central forces and an S ground state, in which case in $_1H^3$, for example, two neutron moments would just cancel, leaving the proton moment. Sachs and Schwinger (S2) and Anderson (A5) found that, although the existence of tensor forces easily accounts for an orbital contribution to the moment and a consequent non-additivity of the intrinsic moments, it is necessary to make very artificial assumptions to account for the observed results on this basis alone. A more natural explanation offered by Villars (W2, T3) is that, in addition to the above orbital contribution, a magnetic moment arises from the mesons which, on the meson theory of forces, exchange back and forth between the particles to give rise to the nuclear forces.

(7) The magnetic moment of the electron measured experimentally (K15a, G2) as discussed in Section 3D is (1.001145 ± 0.000013) Bohr magnetons in remarkable agreement with value calculated (S37, K4) from quantum electrodynamics of $1 + \alpha/2\pi - 2.973\alpha^2/\pi^2 = 1.0011454$.

(8) The magnetic moment of the proton as measured directly by its interaction with an external field within experimental error agrees with the value calculated from the hyperfine structure separation when the electron's intrinsic magnetic moment is taken to have the value given in the preceding paragraph. This agreement is of particular historical significance because it was the experimental lack of such agreement which first suggested that the electron magnetic moment was not exactly 1 Bohr magneton.

(9) The ratio of the measured hfs of hydrogen to that of deuterium disagrees slightly with that calculated from the moment ratios with the use of Eqs. (24) and (30) and with Breit's (B40, B42) reduced mass

correction discussed in Section 2B. This discrepancy can most easily be expressed as (P26a, L10b)

$$\Delta \equiv 1 - \left[\frac{(\Delta \nu_D / \Delta \nu_H)_{\text{exp}}}{(\Delta \nu_D / \Delta \nu_H)_{\text{theor}}} \right] = (1.702 \pm 0.008) \times 10^{-4}$$

If Low and Salpeter's (L10b) reduced mass correction is used, Δ becomes $(1.4 \pm 0.1) \times 10^{-4}$. A number of suggestions have been made relative to the source of the disagreement (H4, B40) of which one of the most promising, due to A. Bohr (B28), is that the electron charge near the nucleus follows the proton in its motion in the deuteron, and hence in computing the magnetic interaction of the neutron with the electrons the neutron cannot be considered to be at the exact center of the atom. Low (L10b) has made quantitative calculations on Bohr's proposal and finds that it leads to a value of Δ equal to $(1.98 \pm 0.10) \times 10^{-4}$. Low and Salpeter (L10b) attribute the discrepancy of $(0.58 \pm 0.20) \times 10^{-4}$ to the structure of the nucleons themselves.

(10) Except for Eu, all measured isotopes whose constitutions differ by just 2 neutrons and which have the same spin have moments which are the same to within 30 percent, and in eleven such cases the agreement is within 12 percent. It is as if the two added neutrons chiefly canceled each other's effect. Various attempts by Inglis (I4) and others have been made to account for this. This tendency of two successive neutrons just to cancel each other's effects lends support to the various shell structure theories of nuclear structure that have been much discussed, particularly since Maria Mayer (M11) and Haxel, Jensen, and Suess (H8a) emphasized the so-called magic numbers in nuclear structure, as discussed further in the Appendix.

(11) It has been pointed out by Schmidt (S8) that almost all nuclear moments of odd mass number nuclei fall between two limits set by a very simple (overly simple) consideration. These limits correspond to assuming that the entire nuclear spin and magnetic moment arise from the extra nucleon, and that one limit arises from the spin and orbital angular momentum being parallel and the other from their being antiparallel. This is illustrated in Fig. 28 and Fig. 29, where the nuclear magnetic moments are plotted as a function of the spin with the first figure giving nuclei with an odd number of protons and even number of neutrons and the second giving nuclei with an odd number of neutrons and an even number of protons. The full lines are the abovementioned Schmidt limits. The derivations of the equations for these lines are given in Eqs. (144) and (145) of the Appendix. As pointed out by Inglis (I1), if it is assumed that the orbital g factor for a neutron in a nucleus is $\frac{1}{8}$ instead of 0, as assumed by Schmidt, and that for a

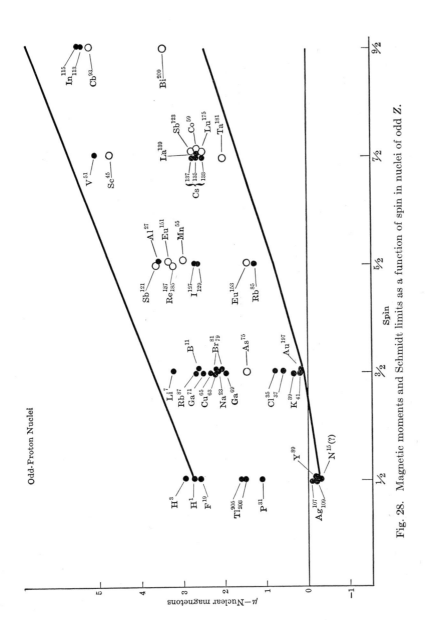

Fig. 28. Magnetic moments and Schmidt limits as a function of spin in nuclei of odd Z.

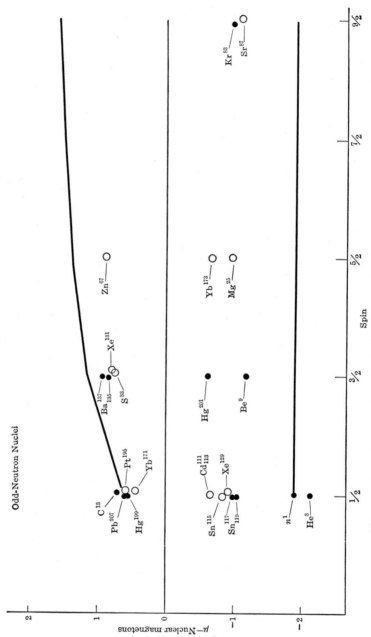

Fig. 29.   Magnetic moments and Schmidt limits as functions of spin in nuclei of odd N.

proton it is $\frac{1}{8}$ instead of 1, the above lines are altered in such a way that they go through the two main groups of nuclei. Margenau and Wigner (M10, R33) have also calculated limiting curves analogous to the Schmidt curves but on the basis of a liquid drop model of the nucleus. Their results, however, are in less good agreement (M10, R33) with experiment than the simple Schmidt lines. This result provides some measure of support for the extreme one-particle models of nuclei that have been considered in detail by Schmidt (S8), Mayer (M11), Haxel, Jensen, and Suess (H8a), Feenberg (F5), Nordheim (N10), and others (B29, W3). Foldy (F10a), Townes (S6), and others have considered the deviations from the Schmidt lines which can arise from a less simplified coupling for the nucleons. Miyazawa (M23a), DeShalit (D7a), and Bloch (B25a) suggest that the departures from the Schmidt lines are due at least in part to a change in the intrinsic magnetic moment of a nucleon when it is in a nucleus. Such a change might be expected in a meson theory of the anomalous nucleon moment since the Pauli exclusion principle will inhibit, say, the dissociation of a proton into a neutron and a meson in dense nuclear matter.

(12) The variation of the nuclear quadrupole moment with the number of nucleons in the nucleus has been studied by Kligman (K13), Gordy (G11), and Townes, Foley, Low (T28) and others. Some of the authors have plotted the quadrupole moment divided by the square of the theoretical nuclear radius as a function of the number of odd nucleons in the nucleus as in Fig. 30. This indeed shows marked periodicities. The arrows on the curve indicate closing of odd nucleon shells at the "magic numbers"—2, 8, 20, 28, 50, 82, or 126. The authors can account for many of the characteristics of these variations of Q but some, such as the magnitudes of the In^{113}, In^{115}, St^{123}, Lu^{176}, are very difficult to account for. Furthermore, the sign of the quadrupole moment of Li^7 is in disagreement with their theory. This, however, may be due to a wrong sign of the $\partial^2 V^e / \partial z^2$ used in calculating Q. Avery and Blanchard (A14) and Present and Feenberg (P17) have attempted to develop a theory consistent with the observed positive quadrupole moment of Li^7. Rainwater (R9a), Bohr (B30a), and Preiswerk (P16a) have attempted to account for the large magnitudes of many nuclear quadrupole moments by considering shell models in which the nucleons moved in fields which were not spherically symmetrical.

(13) The observed nuclear spins have been analyzed from a shell model point of view by Feenberg (F5), Nordheim (N10), Mayer (M11), and Haxel, Jensen, and Suess (H8a). They have been quite successful in accounting for the observed spins. For a detailed discussion of nuclear shell models see the Appendix.

(14) As shown in Table 3, the ratio of the Rb^{87} and Rb^{85} moments differs by 0.33 percent when it is calculated from the ratio of the hyperfine structure splitting than when it is determined from the ratio of

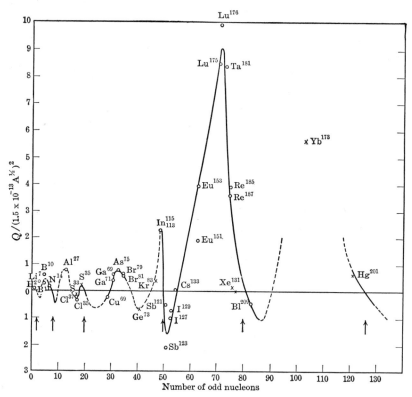

Fig. 30. The plotted points are quadrupole moments divided by the square of the nuclear radius $(1.5 \times 10^{-13} A^{1/3})^2$. Moments of odd proton nuclei and of odd proton-odd neutron nuclei (except Li^6 and Cl^{36}) are plotted as circles against number of protons. Moments of odd neutron nuclei are plotted as crosses against number of neutrons. Arrows indicate closing of major nucleon shells. The solid curve represents regions where quadrupole moment behavior seems established. The dashed curve represents more doubtful regions (T28).

resonance frequencies in an external magnetic field. A similar discrepancy exists for Li^6 and Li^7, for Tl^{203} and Tl^{205}, and for K^{39} and K^{41} (O1). These discrepancies have been interpreted by Bitter (B11), Kopfermann (K29), and Bohr and Weisskopf (B29) as due at least in part to the effect of the finite size of the nucleus, since both the electron density and nuclear magnetic dipole density vary throughout the nucleus and the distribution of the latter may well be different in different isotopes, particularly in a shell model theory of nuclear structure. It has so far, however, been difficult to account for a Cl^{35} and Cl^{37} discrepancy in this manner, since the Cl atom is in a P state for which the electron density at the nucleus is small. However, recent measurements (J1) indicate that the Cl discrepancy is probably due to experimental errors in earlier measurements.

(15) Most nuclei with the number of protons equal to the number of neutrons and with each of these numbers odd have a spin like the deuteron. At one time it was thought that all such nuclei would have a spin of 1. Now, however, as shown in the tables, it is known experimentally that B^{10} and Na^{22} depart from the rule.

(16) The spin measurements of the various radioactive isotopes, such as K^{40} and Na^{22}, have been of great value both in checking beta-ray theory and in inferring spins of other members of radioactive series, because of the theoretical dependence of the beta-ray spectrum on spin changes.

(17) Considerable success has been achieved in interpreting the spins and magnetic moments of the lighter nuclei by Inglis and others (I3, I2, I4, R32, B6, F4, S2, S4). Sachs (S1) has shown that particularly simple relationships hold for mirror or conjugate nuclei (nuclei such that the number of neutrons in the first equals the number of protons in the second while the number of protons in the first equals the number of neutrons in the second). These relationships arise from assumptions that there is charge independence of nuclear forces, that the nuclei are sufficiently light for the asymmetry from the Coulomb force to be neglected, and that the nuclear moment is the resultant of the spin and orbital magnetic moments of the constituent nucleons. The only such mirror pair for which there are data so far is H^3 and He^3. As stated above, this pair could be adapted to Sachs' theory only with the inclusion of the magnetic effect of exchange currents. The discussion of any self-conjugate nucleus, i.e., a nucleus for which the number of neutrons equals the number of protons, is also simplified for the same reasons as are the comparisons of mirror nuclei. These calculations have been summarized by Rosenfeld (R33).

(18) In high-precision nuclear moment measurements careful consideration must be given to the magnetic shielding and related molecular effects discussed in Section 4B. Various discrepancies, due in part to these effects, have been observed in nuclear moment measurements and are discussed in detail in Sections 4B, 5I, and 5J.

(19) An interesting anomaly has been observed in ratio measurements with the nuclear quadrupole moment interactions. Dehmelt

and Kruger (D8) found that the ratio of the nuclear quadrupole moments of Cl^{35} to Cl^{37} varied in different molecular compounds. Most of the proposals for accounting for this anomaly have proved unsatisfactory. A proposal of Gunther-Mohr, Geschwind, and Townes (G33) that the anomaly is due to the polarizability of the nucleus might prove satisfactory. Recent experiments (J1, L9a, Z7) indicate that this anomaly is smaller than originally thought but still definite (about 0.02%). However, with the diminished size of the anomaly, it may be due to molecular distortion instead of nuclear polarizability.

(20) Pound, Purcell, and Ramsey (P16, P30, R15) have performed a series of experiments with lithium fluoride crystals with a very long relaxation time. They found, among other things, that the spin system is essentially isolated for times which vary from 15 sec to 5 min and that for times short compared to these the spin system can be placed in a state of negative temperature. In a negative temperature state the high-energy levels are occupied more fully than the low, and the system has the characteristic that, when radiation is applied to it, stimulated emission exceeds absorption.

5

APPLICATIONS TO CHEMISTRY
AND SOLID STATE PHYSICS

A. Introduction

In recent years nuclear moment measurements have proved to be effective means for studying numerous molecular, chemical, and solid state problems. As discussed in detail below, nuclear moment and related measurements when suitably applied yield data concerning the nature of molecular bonds, locations of atoms in molecules, electron distributions in molecules, the shape of the vibrational potential in molecules, molecular association and dissociation in liquids, chemical exchange, excitation of hindered rotations in solids, strains in solids, crystal structure, electron distribution in metals, and many other important chemical and solid state properties.

This information is obtained by a study of various features of nuclear resonance spectra by the different techniques described in Section 3. These features include the precise frequencies of the nuclear resonances and their shifts in different electronic environments, multiplicities of the resonances, widths of the nuclear resonance lines, and observations of relaxation times. The molecular and solid states information is obtained from the theoretical interpretations of the preceding kinds of data. Some of the molecular results are fairly directly found from the experimental data, as, for example, the nuclear quadrupole interactions, whereas others are much more indirect, as information on chemical bonds, which is indirectly inferred from quadrupole interactions. For this reason many of the subsequent sections will be given double headings, the leading one indicating the more direct results and the subsequent one the less direct inferences.

B. Nuclear Quadrupole Interactions in Molecules. Nature of Chemical Bonds

As discussed on page 48, the first measurements of a nuclear quadrupole interaction in molecules were those of Rabi, Kellogg, Ramsey, and Zacharias on deuterium (K8, K9, K18) with the aid of the molecular beam magnetic resonance method. Subsequently the same method has been applied to other molecules such as diatomic alkali molecules (K39, ZF1) and the alkali halides (N8). The observed frequencies have been interpreted with the aid of Eq. (105) or with related theoretical expressions (K8, K9, R10, F6, F11, R11, R17a) to yield the quadrupole interaction constant $eQ(\partial^2 V^e/\partial z_0{}^2)$. Similar data are obtainable by the molecular beam electric resonance method (H18, T31, ZS6). As discussed on page 66, extensive data on quadrupole interactions in quite different classes of molecules have been obtained in microwave spectroscopy by Gordy, Townes, and others (G7, C12, T21, T24, G8, G9, ZXI). The microwave spectroscopy results have been interpreted with the aid of Eq. (117) and related theoretical expressions (D1, V2, B4, B33) to give the quadrupole interaction constants. Some data on nuclear quadrupole interactions in molecules have been obtained (ZP6) by measurements of the thermal relaxation time T_1 (see page 56) and by a suitable theoretical interpretation of T_1 (ZW1, ZP6), as discussed further in Section 5H.

From the point of view of molecular structure, it is interesting to compare the quadrupole interaction constants involving the same nucleus in different molecules. This comparison shows how $(\partial^2 V_e/\partial z_0{}^2)$ or the quantity q_J defined in Eq. (10) varies from one molecule to another. From the form of Eq. (10) it can be seen that this measures the departure of the molecular charge distribution from spherical symmetry.

As discussed on page 7, Townes (ZT4a, T22) has suggested for atoms covalently bonded in molecules with p orbitals that $\partial^2 V^e/\partial z_0{}^2$ can be approximately calculated from atomic fine structure separations in the same way as in atomic spectra. If the electronic state of the atom in the molecule were a pure p state, the calculation would be quite simple and reliable. However, two uncertainties arise to give difficulty. One uncertainty is that the bond may be ionic instead of covalent (ZP1a); then the ion probably has a closed electron shell and the quadrupole interaction is greatly reduced, because the $\partial^2 V^e/\partial Z_0{}^2$ from the other ion is much less than that of a p electron in the atom itself. Thus NaCl and similar molecules are almost wholly ionically bonded, whereas other molecules are partially ionic and partially covalent. The percentage of ionic bond can often be estimated from the electronegativity difference of the atoms being bonded (ZP1a, ZT4a). The other uncertainty is that the bond may not be a pure one with the electron in a pure p state. There may be a hybridization of the bond with some s as well as p state, in which case the magnitude of $\partial^2 V^e/\partial z_0{}^2$ is decreased. On the other hand, if the hybridization is with a d state, $\partial^2 V^e/\partial z_0{}^2$ is increased (ZT4a).

There is no simple rule for determining the amount of hybridization. In fact, from a molecular point of view one of the chief applications of these experiments is the determination of the degree of hybridization by a measurement of the quadrupole interaction of the same atom in different molecules. In this fashion, for example, Townes (ZT3, ZT4a) has studied the hybridization of bonds in various N, Cl, and As compounds and has found as much as a 15 percent s character in some of them. Likewise a comparison with the alkali halides indicates that they are almost exclusively ionic with less than 3 percent covalent character. Measurements of the quadrupole interactions in different vibrational states of the same molecule by Rabi and his associates (ZF1) have sometimes shown large differences (as much as a factor of 5 between the first and third rotational states).

C. Nuclear Quadrupole Interactions in Rigid Crystals

As discussed on page 61, nuclear quadrupole interactions have been measured in crystals by Pound, Dehmelt, Krüger, and others (ZP7, P15 D8, ZS5). In some experiments (P15) the quadrupole interaction has given rise to a resolvable structure in the magnetic resonance spectrum in strong external magnetic fields. However, in other experiments (D8, ZW2, ZL5, ZX1) the pure quadrupole resonance spectrum in the absence of an external magnetic field has been observed. In still other experiments (P12, P14, ZB12, ZB4) the quadrupole interaction has been inferred from the crystal's thermal relaxation time T_1 (see Section 5H and page 56), since, as discussed in Section 5H, for many pure crystals whose nuclei have spins of more than $\frac{1}{2}$, the nuclear electrical quadrupole interaction with the crystal lattice is the dominant method of relaxation. In general, the measurement of the quadrupole interaction by the last method above is less precise than by either of the other two.

Some of the quadrupole interactions have been measured with single crystals, in which case the nuclear paramagnetic resonance pattern in the presence of a strong external magnetic field consists of a few sharp lines as in Figs. 31b, c, and d. The frequencies of these lines are strongly dependent on the relative orientation between the crystal axis and the external magnetic field, as shown in the figure. However, even with powdered samples definite nuclear paramagnetic resonance absorption and induction patterns are obtained, as shown in Fig. 31a. Such a pattern is a superposition of all the patterns obtained by averaging the single-crystal pattern equally over all possible orientations of the crystal. The dominant resonances with powder samples occur at frequencies which are extrema of the single-crystal resonance frequencies as functions of the crystal orientation (F6, P15).

The theoretical interpretation of the quadrupole interactions in crystals has been given by Pound (P12, B15, ZP9) and others. For crystals

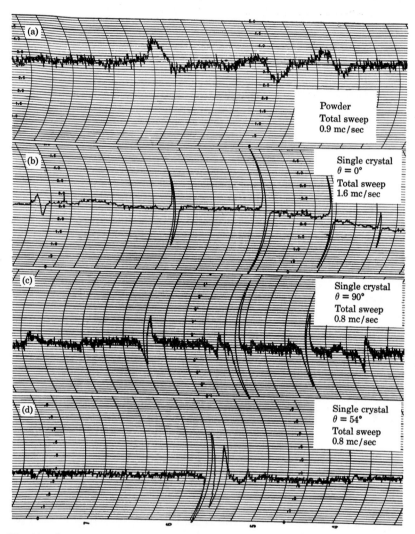

Fig. 31. Spectra of Al₂O₃. (a) A powder pattern 3 mc/sec with a total sweep of 0.9 mc. (b) A single crystal with hexagonal axis parallel to H_0. The total sweep is about 1.6 mc centered at 3 mc. (c) With the crystal axis perpendicular to H_0 and with the sweep rate doubled. (d) With the crystal axis at 54° to H_0 and with the same sweep rate and time constant as (c) (P15).

with axial symmetry, the quadrupole interaction depends upon the crystalline quantity

$$(\partial^2 V^e / \partial z_0{}^2) = \Sigma_j e_j (3 \cos^2 \theta_j - 1) r_j{}^{-3} \qquad (122)$$

where θ_j is the angle between $\mathbf{r}_j$ and the symmetry axis. For crystals with less than axial symmetry, the quadrupole interaction depends on the five independent components of the second-rank tensor that represents the gradient of electric field (P12). Relative to a normal set of orthogonal axes, the tensor can be completely specified by two scalar quantities, one of which is $\partial^2 V^e / \partial z_0{}^2$ with respect to one of the axes while the other is an asymmetry factor.

From the point of view of crystal structure, the value of the quadrupole interaction measurements is that they measure quantities like that in Eq. (122) which depend on the departure of the crystal from spherical symmetry. In a cubic lattice like NaCl, for example, one would anticipate that Eq. (122) would vanish and there would be no quadrupole interaction. However, Watkins and Pound (ZW3) find that often the strains normally in the crystal are sufficiently great to give a strong quadrupole interaction. Observations by Dean and Pound (ZD3) on the temperature dependence of the quadrupole interaction energy indicate a change in bond type as a function of temperature.

D. Direct Nuclear Spin-Spin Interactions in Free Molecules. Internuclear Spacings and Shapes of Molecular Vibrational Potential

The direct magnetic interaction between two nuclear spins in a molecule, discussed on page 48, is of the form

$$\mathfrak{H}_{SS} = r^{-3}[\boldsymbol{\mu}_1 \cdot \boldsymbol{\mu}_2 - 3(\boldsymbol{\mu}_1 \cdot \mathbf{r})(\boldsymbol{\mu}_2 \cdot \mathbf{r}) r^{-2}] \qquad (123)$$

For a fixed orientation of $\boldsymbol{\mu}_1$ and $\boldsymbol{\mu}_2$ but averaged equally over all possible orientations of the internuclear line $\mathbf{r}$, $\mathfrak{H}_{SS}$ averages to zero. As a result, in most nuclear resonance experiments with molecules, for which frequent molecular collisions produce such an averaging, separately resolved resonance lines due to $\mathfrak{H}_{SS}$ cannot ordinarily be observed. However, in molecular beam experiments for which the molecules are collision-free during the period of observation, such direct nuclear spin-spin interactions can be observed. The most detailed observations are those of Rabi, Ramsey, and their co-workers (K8, K9, K18, ZH2, ZH3) on molecular H_2 and HD. These molecules have the advantages that only the first rotational state is dominantly excited at the temperatures of the experiment, and the spin-spin interaction is large owing to the smallness of the internuclear spacing. However, the same technique should be applicable to other molecules like HCl for which the rotational moment of inertia is small. Experiments based on the molecular beam electric resonance method (H18, T31), discussed on page 52, separate out the different rotational states due to the differences in electrical dipole moments of the states and consequently provide the kind of information from which spin-spin interactions can be inferred (ZS6), even for molecules with large moments of inertia. Often, however, the effects of the spin-spin interaction are negligible in comparison to the electrical quadrupole and spin-rotational interactions discussed in Sections 5B and 5M. Direct nuclear spin-spin interaction information on molecules can also be obtained with the nuclear paramagnetic resonance methods when the molecules are frozen into solids, as discussed in Section 5E.

From Eq. (123) it is apparent that a measurement of the direct nuclear spin-spin magnetic interaction provides an experimental value for $\langle r^{-3} \rangle$, the mean inverse cube of the internuclear spacing between the two interacting nuclei. In the absence of other information on the internuclear spacing, the approximate internuclear distance is thereby determined except for a small correction due to zero-point vibration (ZR2). However, even when there is already similar information from other experiments, such as $\langle r^{-2} \rangle$ from band spectra measurements, precision values for $\langle r^{-3} \rangle$ are still of great importance because a comparison of $\langle r^{-3} \rangle$ and $\langle r^{-2} \rangle$ often provides important information about the shape of molecular potential well in which the nuclei are vibrating, as discussed by Ramsey (ZR2). Similar information about the asymmetry of the molecular potential can be obtained by a precision comparison of $\langle r^{-3} \rangle$ in two molecules, such as H_2 and HD, which differ only isotopically and which therefore have similar molecular vibrational potentials but different amplitudes of zero-point vibration (ZR2).

E. Direct Nuclear Spin-Spin Interactions in Rigid Solids.   Atomic Spacings and Bond Angles

If molecules are frozen into a solid the quantity $\mathfrak{H}_{SS}$ of Eq. (123) does not average to zero. Therefore a nuclear paramagnetic resonance absorption or induction spectrum can be obtained for which the spacing of the resonance frequencies depends on $\mathfrak{H}_{SS}$. Just as for the electric quadrupole interactions in crystals, discussed in Section 5C, a definite resonance pattern is obtained with both single-crystal and powdered samples, the latter being the average of the former over all crystal orientations (ZP4, ZA3). Resonance patterns dependent upon the nuclear spin-spin interaction in solids have been obtained by Pake, Purcell, Gutowsky, and others (ZP2, ZP3, ZG11, ZG10).

Theoretical shapes to be anticipated when only a few magnetically interacting nuclei are in each crystal subgroup (molecule, ion, or atomic complex) have been calculated by Pake and others (F6, ZP3, ZA3) for different models and compared with the experimental results. However, as the number of magnetically interacting nuclei in the molecule or crystal group increases, the pattern to be expected becomes more complicated. Unfortunately, as the complexity increases the resolution of detail becomes worse, because the lines are broadened considerably by the effect of nearest neighbors. The problem of calculating the shape of such a complex and unresolved resonance structure is a formidable theoretical problem. However, Van Vleck (ZV3) has shown that the *moments* of the line shape can be fairly quickly and rigorously calculated from a definite model. Thus, for a lattice of identical magnetic moments and spins, Van Vleck (ZV3) has calculated that the second moment of the resonance pattern about its center, $\langle \Delta \nu^2 \rangle$, is given by

$$2\pi \langle \Delta \nu^2 \rangle^{1/2} \equiv \frac{1}{T_2''} = \frac{3}{2} \gamma^2 \hbar \left[\frac{I(I+1)}{3} \right]^{1/2} [\Sigma_{j \neq i} (1 - 3 \cos^2 \theta_{ij})^2 r_{ij}^{-6}]^{1/2} \quad (124)$$

where θ_{ij} is the angle between the external magnetic field and the vector, $\mathbf{r}_{ij}$, connecting the ith nucleus to the jth, where $1/T_2''$ is defined by this equation for later use in Eq. (126), and where the other quantities are as previously defined. For powder samples the above expression can be averaged spherically symmetrically over all directions. When several different magnetic moments are involved, a slightly different expression due to Van Vleck (ZV3) can be used. Equation (124) includes both the broadening effects of the dispersion in the local fields at the nucleus concerned, and the broadening which arises from the shortening of the lifetime of the nuclear orientation state resulting from the fact that a neighboring pair of nuclei can make transitions in opposite senses which thereby conserve energy but interrupt their individual phases. Equation (124) is useful because the left side can be obtained directly from the experimental results and the right side can be calculated for the various competing molecular or crystalline models, so that the one in best agreement with experiment can be selected.

These procedures have been used by Gutowsky and Pake (ZG10) to measure the length of the N—H bond in the NH_4^+ ion of the crystalline ammonium halides, and they have similarly been applied by Andrew (ZA4) and others to a number of organic molecules. The usefulness of nuclear resonance in structural investigations is greatest for atoms like hydrogen, lithium, and other light elements which tend to resist x-ray methods by their failure to scatter with sufficient intensity.

F. Nuclear Paramagnetic Resonance Line Widths in Liquids and Gases.   Collision Narrowing

After the first discovery of nuclear paramagnetic resonance as discussed in Section 3F, one of the properties most extensively studied was the widths of the resonances in liquids and gases, the experiments of Bloembergen, Purcell, and Pound (B26) being among the earliest and most detailed.   Of course, an obvious source of the line width is inhomogeneity of the external magnetic field, but it will be assumed in the following discussion that this experimental source has been eliminated.

From Eq. (114) and for low values of H_1, it is apparent that the width of a nuclear resonance curve depends upon the inverse transverse relaxation time $1/T_2$ (quantitatively, $1/\pi T_2$ is the full width between the half maximum points on a frequency scale).   The theory of line widths in liquids and gases is then the theory of $1/T_2$.

Superficially it might appear that, owing to the electric quadrupole and nuclear spin-spin interactions discussed in the preceding sections, the line widths should be quite large.   However, it is found experimentally that the line widths in liquids and gases are much narrower than the polycrystalline resonance patterns of the same molecules in solids.   As discussed briefly on page 63, the explanation of this initially surprising result is "collision narrowing"; if the molecule is subjected to frequent collisions so that a nuclear spin precesses only a fraction of a cycle under the influence of the local spin-spin and quadrupole moment torques before a collision changes the molecular state to one in which local torques are different, only the average precessional frequency will be observed in a nuclear resonance experiment; therefore the resonance line will be narrower than the group of lines that would be observed in the absence of collisions.

This problem has been considered quantitatively by Bloembergen, Purcell, and Pound (B26), and they have given the following approximate expression for the line breadth parameter $1/T_2$ in liquids and gases:

$$\frac{1}{T_2} = \left(\frac{2}{\pi}\right)^{1/2}\left(\frac{1}{T_2'}\right) + \left(\frac{1}{2T_1}\right) \tag{125}$$

where T_1 is the thermal relaxation time discussed on page 56. $1/T_2'$ is determined implicitly by the approximate equation

$$\left(\frac{1}{T_2'}\right)^2 = \left(\frac{2}{\pi T_2''^2}\right)\tan^{-1}\left(\frac{2\tau_c}{T_2'}\right) \tag{126}$$

where $1/T_2''$, as in Eq. (124), is the width the resonance pattern would have in the absence of collisions, and τ_c is a characteristic of the random collisions and is called the *correlation time*. The value of τ_c can be estimated (B26) either from $1/\tau_c$ as the approximate frequency of the collisions that cause a molecular reorientation or from an estimate by a method due to Debye (ZD4, B26), namely that, for a molecule treated

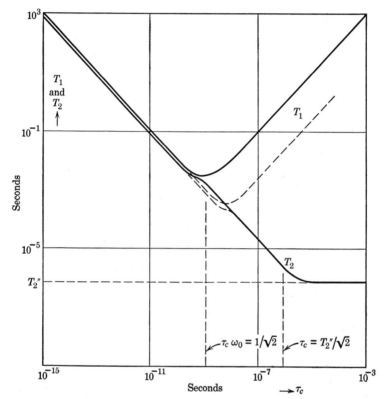

Fig. 32. Dependence of T_1 and T_2 upon τ_c, according to simplified theory in which all interactions are assumed to have the same correlation time. Full curves are for a resonance frequency ω_0, while dashed curves are for a lower resonance frequency ω_1 (B26).

as a sphere of radius a in a liquid of viscosity η'' at an absolute temperature T, the correlation time, τ_c should be approximately $4\pi\eta''a^3/3kT$. Bloembergen et al. (B26) give for $1/T_1$ the approximate expression in liquids and gases

$$\frac{1}{T_1} = \left(\frac{2}{3T_2''^2}\right)\left(\frac{\tau_c}{1 + \omega_0^2\tau_c^2} + \frac{2\tau_c}{1 + 4\omega_0^2\tau_c^2}\right) \qquad (127)$$

where ω_0 is the angular precessional frequency of the nuclei in the external field.

From the form of Eqs. (125), (126), and (127) it is apparent that, for values of $\tau_c \gg T_2'' > 1/\omega_0$,

$$\frac{1}{T_2} = \frac{1}{T_2''} \tag{128}$$

On the other hand, from Eq. (126) it can be seen that, for $\tau_c < T_2''$, pressure narrowing begins and, for $\tau_c \ll 1/\omega_0 < T_2''$, Eqs. (125), (126), and (127) give

$$\frac{1}{T_2} = \left(\frac{4\sqrt{2}}{\pi^{3/2} + 1}\right)\left(\frac{\tau_c}{T_2''^2}\right) = \frac{1.01}{T_1} \tag{129}$$

These approximate quantitative results are in agreement with the qualitative inference two paragraphs above concerning the onset of collision narrowing.

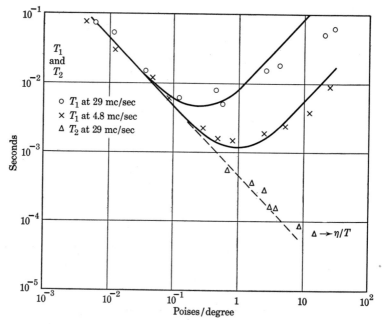

Fig. 33. The relaxation time T_1 and the line-width parameter T_2, plotted against the ratio of viscosity to absolute temperature for glycerin (B26).

If the relaxation times predicted by the above equations are plotted, the results are as in Fig. 32. By using glycerin, the viscosity and hence τ_c of which are thermally varied, Bloembergen, Purcell, and Pound (B26) have obtained an experimental curve, shown in Fig. 33, which compares favorably with the theoretical Fig. 32. They have also measured the relaxation times in a number of other liquids of widely varying viscosity. Bloch, Hansen, and Packard (B18) have studied the effect of added paramagnetic ions on the relaxation time.

The difference between liquid and crystalline nuclear magnetic resonance curves has recently been used by Wilson and Pake (ZW10) to determine the degree of crystallinity in polymers.

G. The Effect of Nuclear Motion on Nuclear Resonance Spectra in Crystals. Hindered Rotation, Oscillation, Exchange, and Tunneling Effects

In Sections 5C and 5E it was assumed for simplicity that the crystal lattice was a rigid structure. This is of course not completely correct, because in all crystals there are thermal vibrations including zero-point vibrations. As long as the vibration amplitudes are small, they only slightly affect the results (ZR2, ZD3). Hence one would expect that, as the temperature is increased in a solid, the resonance spectrum should remain practically constant until melting abruptly allows large amplitude motion and the collision narrowing discussed in the preceding section. Such a normal behavior is indeed found for many substances, but a number of other substances, particularly organic compounds, at temperatures well below the melting point, exhibit a partial narrowing of the resonance pattern.

In ammonium chloride and ammonium bromide, for example Gutowsky and Pake (ZG10) have found in the two substances marked line-width variations as functions of temperature at approximately 130° K and 100° K respectively, which are far below the melting points of the crystals. This suggests that an internal motion of the NH_4^+ ion is taking place at the temperatures at which the line is narrowed. A hindered rotation for the ammonium ion has indeed long been suspected as a result of specific heat discontinuities in the two crystals. However, the specific heat discontinuities in the two crystals are at 243°K and 235°K, which are far above the temperatures of the marked changes in nuclear resonance width. This suggests that the onset of the hindered rotation is a gradual one and that τ_c probably changes more or less continuously in the temperature region concerned, a suggestion which is fully confirmed by an experiment discussed in the next section. With 1,2-dichloroethane the same authors (ZG10) found that the line width narrows at 175°K to approximately half its lower temperature value and finally becomes very sharp above the melting point at 240°K. Many other substances have also been studied (ZA2).

The above rotation frequency required to narrow the line need only be of the magnitude of the $1/\tau_c$ which, in the preceding section, was shown to be adequate to narrow a line; this magnitude was such that narrowing took place for correlation frequencies above $1/T_2''$. From the frozen lattice line widths then, the narrowing should begin to occur at rotation frequencies as low as 50 kc/sec. Since this rotation frequency is vastly below the normal thermal molecular rotation frequencies of 10^9 kc/sec, the rotation at the onset of line narrowing probably consists of abrupt jumps from one equilibrium position to another of rotated orientation.

A particularly interesting case of rotation in solids is the recent study of solid ortho hydrogen by Reif and Purcell (ZR6, ZR7). Here the facts that the protons in the ortho molecule are in symmetrical spin states and that they must satisfy Fermi statistics make it necessary that the molecular rotational quantum number J be odd and hence at least 1 as a minimum. Their results are indeed in accord with such a rotattion in solid hydrogen. However, they find in addition that their experimental observations can best be reconciled with the molecular beam results on free ortho hydrogen molecules if it is assumed that the local crystalline field in the solid removes the approximate degeneracy between the different orientation states of the same J so that the rotational angular momentum is "quenched" (V1), as discussed in Section 5R.

Bloembergen (ZB15), in crystals of $CuSO_4 \cdot 5H_2O$, and Poulis (ZP5), in $CuCl_2 \cdot 2H_2O$, have found spin-spin effects due to the *electronic* moments of the cupric ions interacting with proton moments and thereby shifting the resonance frequencies of the latter. These observations are greatly facilitated by strong exchange currents of the cupric ions which reduce the otherwise excessive broadening of the proton resonance by exchange narrowing analogous to the narrowing from hindered rotations. Evidence for anti-ferromagnetism in the second of these salts at low temperatures has been obtained (ZP5) from these experiments.

H. Thermal Relaxation Times

The nuclear paramagnetic resonance methods may also be used to study the thermal relaxation time T_1 of Eqs. (107) and (127), in various gaseous, liquid, and solid samples. T_1 can be measured in a variety of ways (B26, ZP4, T20, H1, H2, B5). The sample can be saturated with a large resonant signal, and then with a much weaker signal the rate of growth of the resonance can be observed as a function of time, from which T_1 can be inferred (B26). T_1 can be obtained by a study of the received signal strength as a function of the driving field strength and its interpretation with the aid of Eq. (114) (B26). The various transient methods discussed on page 60 and introduced by Torrey (T20), Hahn (H1, H2), and others (B5a, ZX1) can all be used to measure T_1.

The significance of the measurements of T_1 can be discussed only in terms of the theories by which it is interpreted. Before the application of an external magnetic field H_0, there is no net nuclear magnetization in a sample, and immediately after the sudden application of H_0 there will still be none, and so it will remain until by some means the spins can exchange energy with the only thermal reservoir available, the vibrational modes of the lattice or the translational and rotational motion of liquids and gases. As this energy exchange proceeds, the nuclear magnetization approaches its equilibrium value in accordance with Eq. (107). If in a crystal this rate of exchange of energy between the spin system and the lattice vibrations is small compared to the rate of interaction within the spin system itself, i.e., if $T_1 \gg T_2$, as is often true for crystals, one can speak of a temperature T of the spin system; then the temperature immediately after the application of H_0 is infinite and the relaxation time T_1 is a measure of the rate at which the spin system cools to the lattice temperature.

One of the earliest theories of the thermal relaxation of a nuclear spin system in crystals is that due to Waller (ZW1) and Heitler and Teller (ZH6). They considered that the source of the coupling between the spins and the lattice vibrations was the fluctuation in the internal magnetic fields which arises from the vibrations as a result of the strength of the magnetic field at one nucleus depending on the distance to the neighboring nuclear magnetic dipole moment which produces it. Waller considered two processes. The first or direct process involves lattice vibrations at the nuclear precession frequency ν_0 and is so feeble as to be negligible in nuclear paramagnetism. The second process involves a pair of lattice modes which differ in frequency by an amount ν_0; the non-linearity of the r^{-3} factor in the dipole interaction causes transitions at the beat frequency ν_0. This "second-order" process is far more important than the direct process, and in favorable cases it leads to theoretical relaxation times as low as 10^4 sec. However, ordinarily the relaxation time is experimentally much shorter than this, and even in the few cases (ZS1, ZP11) where such long times have been measured there is no clear evidence that the relaxation has been due to the Waller mechanism.

A much more effective mechanism for thermal relaxation in crystals is the presence of paramagnetic impurities, as shown by Bloembergen (ZB12) and Hatton and Rollin (ZH4). Bolembergen has shown theoretically that the paramagnetic impurities are much more effective in producing thermal relaxation than might be expected. Not only can a single paramagnetic ion bring the nuclear spins in its immediate vicinity to thermal equilibrium, but also the interaction of the nuclear spins with each other spreads this tendency toward thermal equilibrium to much more distant nuclei. It is probable that in many crystals this is the dominant means of thermal relaxation.

Another means of relaxation is a result of the fact that the crystals are not completely rigid; as discussed in the preceding section, hindered rotations, tunneling, and other motions allow atoms, ionic groups, and even molecular groups to jump from one position or orientation to another. The effect of such internal lattice jumps is to give rise to an effective correlation time τ_c, as in the preceding section, and to exchange energy between the spin system and the lattice. The theory of relaxation by this process has been discussed extensively by Bloembergen, Purcell, and Pound (B26); an approximation to their result for $1/T_1$ has already been given in Eq. (127).

A final means of thermal relaxation in crystals is the effect on the nuclear electrical quadrupole interaction of fluctuations in the electric field gradient as a result of thermal vibrations in the crystal lattice. The theory of this means of relaxation has been discussed by Pound (P15) in essentially the same manner as by Waller (ZW1), except that the quadrupole interaction replaces that of the magnetic dipole. Just as in Waller's theory the "second-order" process is the dominant one. The relaxation times in the electric quadrupole and the magnetic dipole cases are then in the ratio $(\mu^2/e^2Q)^2$, which can be of the order of 10^{-5}; thus the previously too large 10^4 sec can be reduced to a fraction of a second. Therefore, in sufficiently pure crystals with nuclear quadrupole moments, the relaxation can be due to this process.

In liquids and gases there are even more extreme varieties of motions and rotations than those discussed two paragraphs above, and consequently the dominant mode of relaxation is by such random motions and collisions to which the theory in Section 5F [that of Bloembergen, Pound, and Purcell (B26)] and the approximate Eq. (127) apply. The theoretical and experimental dependences of $1/T_1$ upon τ_c are given in Figs. 32 and 33, respectively. Depending on circumstances, the actual mechanism which gives rise to the interaction with the nuclear spin system may be the mutual magnetic interactions of the nuclear dipole moments, magnetic interactions with paramagnetic impurities, nuclear quadrupole interactions, or similar interactions. The corresponding interaction constants have sometimes been determined from the observed T_2 (ZP6).

Typical of the applications of the studies of nuclear relaxation times in solids is the experiment of Sachs, Turner, and Purcell (ZS1) on ammonium chloride and ammonium bromide. By measuring T_1 for these crystals between 90°K and 250°K and by the use of Eq. (127), they were able to infer the values of the correlation time τ_c at all temperatures in this interval. They found that τ_c varied continuously from 10^{-4} sec at the lowest temperature to 10^{-10} sec at the highest temperature, in agreement with the variation for τ_c anticipated in the preceding section from the low temperature for the discontinuity in T_2.

With very pure crystals of lithium fluoride Pound (ZP8) has obtained values of T_1 as large as 5 min. However, when these crystals are exposed to x-rays until they become slightly yellow, the relaxation time is reduced to 10 sec. This effect may provide a valuable tool for studying the color centers in crystals. Before its x-ray bombardment, a crystal of lithium fluoride with a long relaxation time was also used by Pound, Purcell, and Ramsey (P30, R15) in the experiments on audiofrequency spectroscopy, resonant heating of the nuclear spin system, and negative temperatures of the nuclear spin system discussed on pages 62 and 98.

The theory of the nuclear thermal relaxation time in metals has been developed by Korringa (ZK6) and others. At low temperatures, they show that the relaxation is primarily due to the conduction electrons and consequently is dependent upon the electron distribution in the metal. As discussed in the next section, the exact frequency of a nuclear resonance in a metal is also dependent upon the electron distribution, and Korringa (ZK6) has shown that the two dependences are closely related. In fact, he shows that, if the $\Delta H/H$ of Eq. (131) is the fractional shift of the resonance position in the metal, the relaxation time T_1 is given approximately by

$$T_1 = \mu_0{}^2 \left[\pi \hbar k T \gamma_I{}^2 \left(\frac{\Delta H}{H} \right)^2 \right]^{-1} \tag{130}$$

With this and Eq. (131), information concerning the electron distribution in metals can be inferred from the measurement of T_1. Korringa (ZK6) finds that the experimental results of Bloembergen (ZB12) and Poulis (ZK6) on T_1 are in agreement with Eq. (130) when the experimental results discussed in Section 5I are used for $\Delta H/H$.

I. Shift of Resonance Frequency in Metals.   Electron Distribution in Metals

As mentioned on page 75, Knight (K14) discovered that the nuclear paramagnetic resonance frequencies of sodium, aluminum, copper, and other metals are several tenths of a percent higher when the nuclei are in a metallic state than when the same nuclei are in the form of either powdered or dissolved salts. Such a resonance shift for copper is illustrated in Fig. 26. Townes (K14, T29, K17a) suggested that this was due to the paramagnetism of the conduction electrons when they are in the immediate vicinity of a nucleus.

As discussed by Townes and others (T29), the magnetic field ΔH at the nucleus due to the electron spins can be estimated as follows. From Eqs. (24) and (21), ΔH is $8\pi/3$ times the mean density of spin moment at the nucleus, assuming cubic or higher symmetry. In terms of wave functions of individual electrons in the metal, the spin moment density at the nucleus can be written $\chi_p M H \langle | \psi_F(0) |^2 \rangle$, where χ_p is the spin contribution to the macroscopic susceptibility per unit mass, M is the mass of one atom, and $\langle | \psi_F(0) |^2 \rangle$ is the average probability density at the nucleus for all electronic states on the Fermi surface. However, the hyperfine structure splitting $\Delta\nu$ for an s electron in the free atom is given by the combination of Eqs. (37) and (24). When all of these are combined, the immediate result is

$$\frac{\Delta H}{H} = \frac{hc\, \Delta\nu\, I \chi_p M}{\mu_I \mu_0 (2I + 1)} \frac{\langle | \psi_F(0) |^2 \rangle}{| \psi_{n0}(0) |^2} \tag{131}$$

From this expression it is apparent that a measurement of the Knight shift provides information concerning the electron distribution in metals; in particular it gives the probability density of a conduction electron near the top of the Fermi distribution being at a nucleus.

Townes, Herring, and Knight (T29) have shown that the above theoretical expression agrees with experiment in most cases. However, Kohn and Bloembergen (K17a) have shown that there is a disagreement in the case of metallic lithium which may indicate a deficiency in the previously assumed theoretical description of the electron distribution of metallic lithium.

As discussed in the preceding section, the magnitude of the Knight shift theoretically should be, and experimentally is, approximately related to the thermal relaxation time T_1 in the same metal by Eq. (130).

J. Magnetic Shielding and Chemical Shifts

As discussed in Section 4B, Knight (K14), Dickinson (D12), and Proctor and Yu (P24) found that even with non-metallic samples the apparent nuclear magnetic moment is different in different chemical compounds. These chemical shifts are sometimes as large as several tenths of a percent, though they are usually smaller. Ramsey (R12, R14) and Proctor and Yu (P24) attributed these shifts to the different electronic environment of the nucleus in various compounds and, consequently, to the different magnetic shielding.

Ramsey (R12, R14, R17b) developed the theory of magnetic shielding discussed in Section 4B and derived for it the general expression in

Eq. (119). As discussed on page 72, one characteristic of such a theory is that the magnitude of the shift is proportional to the external magnetic field, and hence the shielding cannot be experimentally measured by resonance experiments in different magnetic fields; these experiments and many others agree with the theory in this respect.

Unfortunately, numerical values cannot be easily calculated from Eq. (119) for comparison with experiment. However, even in the absence

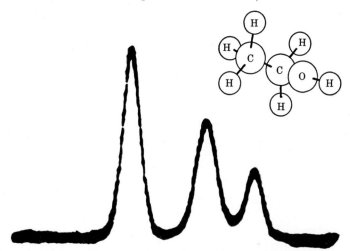

Fig. 34.   Nuclear paramagnetic resonance curve for hydrogen in ethyl alcohol (CH_3CH_2OH). The largest resonance presumably comes from the three protons in CH_3, the next from CH_2, and the smallest from OH. The position of the weakest of the three resonances is dependent on the temperature of the liquid sample (ZA5).

of detailed numerical calculations, Eq. (119) is valuable in inferring molecular data from the experimental results. Thus a large negative value for σ as found by Proctor and Yu (P22) in $Co(NH_3)_6Cl_3$ from Eq. (119) suggests a low value for at least one $E_n - E_0$, i.e., suggests that there is a low-lying electronic state in the molecule (R17b).

The chemical shift can often be used to identify atoms in different parts of the same molecule. For example, Fig. 34 shows the nuclear induction spectrum obtained by Arnold, Dharmatti, and Packard (ZA5) with ethyl alcohol. Since the formula for ethyl alcohol is CH_3CH_2OH, this spectrum is quite reasonable, the strongest peak being associated with hydrogens in the CH_3 group, the intermediate peak with CH_2, and the weakest peak with OH.

Ramsey (R16, R17b) has shown theoretically that, if the molecules are not subject to frequent collisions to produce the averaging of Section 5F, the shielding constant should not be a simple scalar, but a tensor of the second rank, or dyadic. He has given a general expression for this dyadic (R17b). He has also shown (R16) that, if the difference in the magnetic shielding constant is measured for two different orientation states of the molecule and if the measured difference is suitably combined with the spin-rotational interaction value from Section 5M, the mean value of $\langle(3z^2 - r^2)/r^3\rangle$ for the electron distribution in the molecule is determined. So far, however, no experimental determination of a dependence of σ upon orientation has been made.

K. Temperature and Concentration Dependence of Magnetic Shielding. Molecular Association, Dissociation, and Chemical Exchange

According to Eq. (119), the magnetic shielding should be temperature-independent. However, as pointed out by Ramsey (R17b), this is true only if all molecular states within an energy of the order of kT of the ground state have the same shielding constant. Ordinarily they do, and the observed shielding constants are usually temperature-independent. However, if several states with different shielding constants are separated from the ground state by less than kT, the molecules will spend parts of their time in each state. If, as in Section 5F, the frequency $1/\tau_c$ of exchange between the different states is large compared to the differences of Larmor precession frequency in the states of different shielding constant, only a single resonance frequency will be observed, and it will be at the time average of the Larmor frequencies of the different states. In such circumstances a change in temperature in general will lead to a change in the distribution of times between the different states and consequently in the observed mean shielding constant.

Proctor and Yu have found, for example, that the shielding constant of $Co(NH_3)_6Cl_3$ varies by about 0.01 percent between 20° and 80°C. This suggests (R17b) a low-lying molecular state with a different shielding constant, in agreement with the similar suggestion made for the same compound in Section 5J on the basis of the large magnitude of σ rather than its temperature dependence.

A particularly interesting example of temperature dependence was discovered by Packard and Arnold (ZP1). They found that the weakest resonance in the ethyl alcohol triplet shown in Fig. 34 was temperature-dependent even though the magnitude of the shift itself was not unusually large in contrast to the example of the preceding paragraph. Ramsey and Liddel (R17b, R17c) suggested that this temperature dependence is probably due to the molecular association of the liquid alcohol, in which association the hydrogen of the OH radical participates. The observed magnetic shielding of this proton as discussed above is then the time average value of the shieldings of the associated and non-asso-ciated states. Since a change in temperature affects the degree of asso-ciation, it alters the average shielding. The fact that a single temper-ature-dependent resonance is observed instead of two separate reso-nances is an indication by the above theory that the correlation time τ_c for transitions between the associated and unassociated states is less than a millisecond. Ramsey and Liddel (R17b, R17c) suggested also that their hypothesis could be checked by dissolving the alcohol in a solvent such as carbon tetrachloride, which is known to alter the extent of association. This has been done by Packard and Arnold (ZP1); such dilution shifts the resonance in the same direction as increasing the temperature, in agreement with what would be expected on the Ramsey and Liddel hypothesis.

An important further extension of the effects of concentration and tem-perature on magnetic shielding constants has recently been carried out by Gutowsky and Saika (ZG13). They find that in this fashion they are able to study the dependence of the degree of dissociation of an acid upon its concentration. Furthermore, the dependence of the nature of the results upon the correlation time τ_c provides information about the rates of chemical exchange in various processes. In addition, from the magnitudes of the chemical shifts they are able to infer, for example, that in the ion H_3O^+ each of the O—H bonds is about one-third ionic, the remaining two-thirds being relatively unchanged from H_2O itself.

L. Electron-Coupled Nuclear Spin-Spin Interactions

In independent experiments Gutowsky, McCall, Slichter, and McNeil (ZG12, ZM1) and Hahn and Maxwell (ZH1) have found in liquids and gases a multiplet structure of the nuclear paramagnetic resonance spec-trum. They found that their observations could be accounted for if an interaction of the form $h\delta \mathbf{I}_N \cdot \mathbf{I}_{N'}$ is assumed to exist between the nuclei N and N' under the conditions of their experiments.

At first sight it might appear that such a multiplet structure is quite reasonable and might be attributed either to nuclear electrical quadru-pole interaction as in Section 5B or to direct nuclear spin-spin magnetic interaction as in Section 5D. However, in Section 5F it was shown that the effects of frequent collisions in liquids and gases eliminated such a structure and yielded only a single narrow resonance. That this is true regardless of the relative orientation of the nuclear spins of two mag-netically interesting nuclei is a consequence of the fact that Eq. (123) gives zero when averaged equally over all orientations of the internu-clear line r. If magnetic shielding of the nuclear spin-spin interaction by the orbital motion of the electrons is included, the form of Eq. (123)

is modified in such a way that a residual spin-spin interaction of the desired form is obtained. However, several attempts to account for the experimental results in this way led to interactions that were much too weak (ZG12, ZM1, ZH1, ZD6).

The solution to this difficulty was suggested by Ramsey and Purcell (R16b, ZR4), who suggested a mechanism which should give rise to an $I_N \cdot I_{N'}$ interaction of the magnitude observed. This mechanism is the magnetic interaction between each nucleus and the electron spin of its own atom together with the exchange coupling of the electron spins with each other. This mechanism can most easily be described for a $^1\Sigma$ diatomic molecule such as HD. It corresponds to the fact that the magnetic interaction of the one nucleus with the electron of its atom will make the electron of that atom tend to lie more frequently anti-parallel to the nuclear spin than parallel to it. On the other hand, the two electron spins in the singlet state must be anti-parallel to each other so that the electron of the other atom will tend to lie more frequently parallel to the spin of the first nucleus. However, the electron of that atom magnetically interacts with the second nucleus. The combination of these interactions therefore provides a spin interaction between the two nuclei. In terms of perturbation theory the proposed mechanism corresponds to a second-order perturbation by the higher electronic triplet states of molecules, the perturbing interaction being the magnetic interaction of each nucleus with the electron spins. The reason why electron-spin effects enter here, whereas they are omitted in ordinary magnetic shielding calculations, is that here the magnetic fields from both nuclei vary over the molecule, whereas in the ordinary magnetic shielding case one of the perturbing fields is the externally applied one, which is uniform over the molecule and hence affects both electron spins alike.

Detailed calculations including both this contribution and that of the orbital motions of the electrons have been made by Ramsey (ZR4). He has shown that in general the electron-coupled nuclear spin-spin interaction is of the form $h\Sigma_{ij}\delta_{ij}I_{Ni}I_{N'j} + h\delta I_N \cdot I_{N'}$, where δ_{ij} is a traceless tensor of the second rank. Only when frequent collisions average the molecular orientation equally over all directions, as in Section 5F, does the interaction reduce to the simpler $h\delta I_N \cdot I_{N'}$. The general theoretical expression for δ is quite complicated; it is given in the literature (ZR4). However, in the case of HD, over 90 percent of the interaction is of the form

$$\delta_{HD} = (64\mu_0^2 h\gamma_H\gamma_D/9\Delta)|\psi|^2_{1H2D} \qquad (132)$$

where Δ is a suitable (ZR4) mean energy of the excited electronic states of the HD molecule, $|\psi|^2_{1H2D}$ is the probability density for one electron to be on the proton and the other on the deuteron. The rest of the quantities have their earlier meanings.

Following the suggestion of Ramsey and Purcell (R16b), measurements of δ in HD have been made by Smaller (ZS9), Carr and Purcell (ZC1), Wimett (ZW8), and their associates with the result that δ is 43 ± 0.5 cps. Figure 35 shows resonance patterns for HD with the

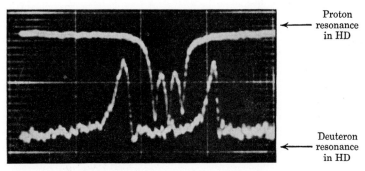

Proton
resonance
in HD

Deuteron
resonance
in HD

Fig. 35. Proton and deuteron nuclear paramagnetic resonances with gaseous HD. The multiplicity of these curves is presumably due to electron-coupled nuclear spin-spin interaction. The scales used for the two curves are indicated by the fact that the two deuteron resonances are 43 cps apart, whereas the outermost proton resonances are each 43 cps from the central one (ZW8).

triple proton resonance and the double deuteron one. Equation (132) can be made to agree with this experimental value provided that Δ is assumed to have the reasonable value of 1.4 Rydbergs.

M. Spin-Rotational Magnetic Interaction

In some experiments with molecules not subjected to frequent collisions, it is possible to measure the spin-rotational magnetic interaction, i.e., the interaction of the nuclear magnetic moment with the magnetic field which exists as a result of the rotation of the molecule. The most extensive measurements are those of Rabi (K9, K8), Ramsey (R10, K18, ZH2, ZH3), and their associates on the first rotational states of H_2, D_2, and HD as described on pages 47ff. and illustrated in Figs. 16 and 18. The analysis of the curves in Figs. 16 and 18 determines the spin-rotation interaction constant H' of Eq. (105) for these molecules. The corresponding spin-rotation interaction constants for alkali halide molecules have been measured by Nierenberg and Ramsey (N8), Rabi (ZZ2), and others (ZH15) by analyzing molecular beam magnetic resonance spectra of molecules excited to a number of different rotational states. Trischka (T31, ZS6), Schwartz (ZS6), and others have measured spin-rotational interactions in specific rotational states by the molecular beam electric method described on page 52. Henderson (ZH7, ZH8) and others (ZG3) have evaluated spin-rotational interaction constants from microwave spectra at low pressures, as discussed in Section 5Q.

At first sight it might be thought that the spin-rotational magnetic interaction constant could be calculated by treating the electron distribution as a rigid structure rotating at the known rotational angular velocity of the molecule and consequently producing a calculable magnetic field at the nucleus concerned. However, if this is done it is found that the electron contribution to the spin-rotational interaction should be much greater than it is experimentally. This in itself clearly indicates one important significance of the measurement of this quantity: it shows that rotating molecules possess a considerable backward circulation or slippage of the electrons.

The theoretical interpretation of the spin-rotational magnetic interaction has been discussed by Brooks (B47), Wick (W9), Foley (F11), Ramsey (R14, R17b, ZR2, ZR3), and Schwartz (ZS7). They show (R14) that the spin-rotational magnetic interaction constant is directly proportional to the second terms in Eqs. (119) and (120), and that the molecular properties defined by these terms are then measurable. A more important meaning, as pointed out by Ramsey (R14, R17b, R16c) and discussed on page 73, is that the experimental value of the spin-rotational interaction constant can be used to evaluate the unknown quantity upon which the magnetic shielding constant and hence the precision values of the nuclear moment depend. The result of such a use of spin-rotational interaction data is given in Eq. (121). A similar use of this data was made at the end of Section 5J in indicating how values for $\langle (3z^2 - r^2)r^{-3} \rangle$ could be obtained from the dependence of the magnetic shielding upon molecular orientation.

The close relationship between spin-rotational interaction and magnetic shielding at first sight might appear to be a surprising accident. However, it can be seen to be quite reasonable from the following point of view. Larmor's theorem essentially states that the application of a magnetic field $\mathbf{H}$ produces a similar effect on the electrons as a rotation of angular velocity

$$\boldsymbol{\omega} = \frac{e\mathbf{H}}{2mc} \tag{133}$$

The electronic contribution to the spin-rotational interaction is determined by the magnetic field at the nucleus resulting from the electronic motion which is a consequence of the rotation at angular velocity $\boldsymbol{\omega}$. On the other hand, the magnetic shielding depends on the magnetic field at the nucleus resulting from the electronic motion which is a consequence of the application of an external field **H**. Since ω and **H** are related by Eq. (133), the shielding and the spin-rotational interaction constants can be related. This argument can indeed be made quantitative, and Eq. (121) can be derived in this way (R14).

The above theories of the spin-rotational interaction constant all assume that the entire interaction is due to the magnetic field at the nucleus from the circulation of the electrical charges of the molecule as a result of the molecular rotation. However, Ramsey (ZR3) points out that there are additional terms which for H_2 are about 1 percent as large as the Wick term. These contributions depend upon the acceleration of the nucleus. One of them arises from the fact that the acceleration in a molecule is electrical and the moving nuclear magnetic moment interacts with the electric field that produces the acceleration. The other is the relativistic Thomas precession, which is similar to the Thomas precession that occurs for electrons in atoms. The accelerations that give rise to these interactions result from the centripetal acceleration in the rotating molecule and the zero-point vibration. For H_2 Ramsey has calculated that these acceleration effects should give a contribution to the spin-rotational interaction constant of 1060 cps out of a total of $113{,}904 \pm 30$ cps.

N. Rotational Magnetic Moments. Mean Square Radii of Electron Distribution in Molecules

Rotational magnetic moments of molecules have been measured by the molecular beam magnetic resonance method and by the methods of microwave spectroscopy. Using the former method, Ramsey (R10, ZH2) and Harrick (ZH2) have measured the rotational magnetic moments of H_2, D_2, and HD. The method of measurement is essentially identical with the molecular beam nuclear magnetic resonance method, except that the oscillator frequency is chosen to be appropriate to the Larmor precession frequency of the magnetic moment which results from the circulation of charge in the rotating molecule. The method provides highly accurate values of the rotational magnetic moments. Useful, though less accurate, values of the rotational magnetic moments have been obtained by the methods of microwave spectroscopy for NH_3, OCS, H_2O, HDO, and SO_2 by Jen (J10, ZJ2, ZJ3) and by Eshbach and Strandberg (ZE2).

The theory of rotational magnetic moments for linear molecules has been developed by Wick (ZW7) and Ramsey (R10, ZR2). The extension of the theory to non-linear polyatomic molecules has been presented by Eshbach and Strandberg (ZE2), Schwartz (ZS7), and Ramsey (ZR2). They show that in polyatomic molecules the rotational gyromagnetic ratio is, in general, a tensor of the second rank.

Superficially it might appear that the rotational magnetic moment could be calculated by supposing that the electronic charge distribution rotates rigidly with the molecule. However, as with the closely analogous spin-rotational interaction of Section 5M, such an assumption leads to much too large an electronic contribution to the rotational magnetic moment. Thus the experimental results on rotational magnetic moments agree with the spin-rotational interaction results of the preceding section in indicating a large backward circulation or slippage of the electrons.

Just as it was shown in Section 5M that there was a close relation between magnetic shielding and spin-rotational interaction, so here there is for the same reason a similar relation between molecular diamagnetic susceptibility and rotational magnetic moment; the rotational angular velocity of the molecule and the magnetic field of the corresponding susceptibility are related by Eq. (133). As discussed by Van Vleck (V1) and Ramsey (ZR2), the diamagnetic susceptibility of a diatomic molecule is given by

$$\chi = - \frac{e^2}{6mc^2} \langle \Sigma_k r_k{}^2 \rangle + \chi^{HF} \tag{134}$$

where χ^{HF} is the so-called "high-frequency" term (V1) in the molecular magnetic susceptibility. χ^{HF} has a form similar to the last term in Eq. (119), except that none of the matrix elements is divided by $r_k{}^3$. The relation, just mentioned, between the rotational magnetic moments and the diamagnetic susceptibility, as shown by Wick (ZW7) and others (R10, ZR2), is such that for linear molecules the electronic contribution to the rotational magnetic moment is proportional to χ^{HF}. Consequently the measured values of the rotational magnetic moments determine the values of the χ^{HF}'s (R10, ZR2). Harrick and Ramsey's (ZH2) value for χ^{HF} determined in this way for H_2 can be combined (ZR5) with Eq. (134) and the precision experimental value of Havens (ZH5) for the magnetic susceptibility. In this way, Ramsey (ZR5) has found that the mean square distance $\langle r^2 \rangle$ of an electron from the midpoint of the H_2 molecule is

$$\langle r^2 \rangle = (0.7258 \pm 0.0022) \times 10^{-16} \text{ cm}^2 \tag{135}$$

O. Dependence of Diamagnetic Susceptibility on Molecular Orientation. Principal Second Moments of Electron Distribution in Molecules

In molecular beam magnetic resonance experiments in which the resonance corresponds to a molecular reorientation, as in the preceding section, it is sometimes possible to detect small shifts in the resonance frequencies which correspond to the differences of the molecular diamagnetic susceptibility in two different orientation states. In this way Ramsey and Harrick (R10, ZH2) have determined the dependence of the diamagnetic susceptibility of an H_2 molecule upon its rotational magnetic quantum number when it is in the first rotational state.

The theoretical interpretation of these results has been discussed by Ramsey (R12a, ZH2, ZR2, ZR5). He has shown that, when the above results are combined with the value of χ^{HF} found as in the previous section, a value for the quadrupole moment of the molecular electron distribution Q_e can be determined. For H_2, the value of Q_e is

$$Q_e = -2 \langle 3z^2 - r^2 \rangle = (0.330 \pm 0.013) \times 10^{-16} \text{ cm}^2 \qquad (136)$$

This compares favorably with the theoretical values of $(0.344 \pm 0.010) \times 10^{-16}$ cm^2 calculated by James and Coolidge (ZJ1).

When this result is combined with that of the previous section for $\langle r^2 \rangle$, all the principal second moments of the electron distribution can be found. In this way Ramsey (ZR5) has obtained, for the H_2 molecule in its first rotational and zeroth vibrational state and with the z axis taken along the internuclear line,

$$\langle x^2 \rangle = \langle y^2 \rangle = (0.2144 \pm 0.0015) \times 10^{-16} \text{ cm}^2$$
$$\langle z^2 \rangle = (0.2969 \pm 0.0022) \times 10^{-16} \text{ cm}^2 \qquad (137)$$

Measurements of molecular quadrupole moments of a number of other molecules have been made by Hill, Smith, and Howard (ZH12a, ZH12b) from the collision broadening of microwave spectral lines. These measurements are much less accurate than those obtained by the above method, but they can more easily be extended to different molecules. They are discussed in greater detail in Section 5Q.

P. Effects of Vibration and Centrifugal Stretching

Most of the quantities discussed above depend either directly or indirectly upon the internuclear spacing. This spacing varies with time if the molecule is vibrating. Even when a molecule is in its lowest vibrational state there is some zero-point vibration. Consequently the various interactions must be averaged over the zero-point vibration and, for example, if r is an internuclear distance, $\langle r^{-3} \rangle^{-\frac{1}{3}}$ cannot be equated to $\langle r^{-2} \rangle^{-\frac{1}{2}}$. Also, in rotating molecules allowance must be made for centrifugal stretching. Detailed discussions of methods for allowing for the zero-point vibration and centrifugal stretching have been presented by Ramsey (ZR2).

For many experiments the zero-point vibration and centrifugal stretching are merely complications that must be theoretically allowed for by the means described by Ramsey (ZR2). However, in certain cases the existence of the zero-point vibration is a distinct advantage, and it makes possible the calculation of additional information from the experimental results. Thus, when $\langle r^{-3} \rangle$ is experimentally determined from the nuclear spin-spin magnetic interaction as in Section 5D and compared with the molecular spectra value of $\langle r^{-2} \rangle$, information on the asymmetry of the Morse potential is obtained as a result of the zero-point vibration. Likewise, a comparison of experimental values of $\langle r^{-3} \rangle$ for H_2 and HD should supply similar information because of the different amplitudes of zero-point vibration in the two cases.

Measurements of rotational magnetic moments have been made for H_2 in both the first and the second rotational state by Barnes, Bray, Harrick, and Ramsey (ZB3, ZH2). They find that the rotational magnetic moment in the second rotational state is not exactly double that in the first. If the difference is assumed to be due to centrifugal stretching, the results can be interpreted as showing that the dependence of the χ^{HF} of Eq. (134) upon the internuclear spacing r is as $r^{3.8}$ (ZB3, ZR2). The same result is obtained by comparing the rotational moments for H_2 and D_2, which differ in both centrifugal stretching and zero-point vibration. A similar analysis of the spin-rotational magnetic interaction in H_2 and D_2 has been made, and the dependence of the second term in Eq. (119) on the internuclear spacing r has been determined (ZR2, ZH3).

The effects of molecular vibration and rotation play a particularly important role in the microwave spectroscopy studies of the next section, and consequently a discussion of the effects of vibration and rotation in microwave spectra is deferred to that section.

Q. Microwave Spectroscopy

The methods of microwave spectroscopy, described in Section 3G, have been applied in many important ways in the study of molecular and solid state properties. In fact, microwave spectroscopy was originally developed for the study of these properties, and merely incidentally it was found to yield data on nuclear spins, quadrupole moments, and magnetic moments. For this reason an extensive discussion of chemical and solid state studies by microwave techniques would be inappropriate here because their relation to nuclear moment studies is too small. Consequently in this section only a brief summary of the kinds of applications will be given. For a detailed listing of the results the reader is referred to several excellent review articles on microwave spectroscopy which have recently appeared (ZT4a, ZK1a, G9, ZG14, ZT4, ZM0b).

Since the molecular beam experiments of Rabi and his associates (ZL4, ZF1), in which the rotational quantum number J is changed, are at microwave frequencies and are subject to the same interpretation as microwave absorption spectra, they will also be included in this section. The same would be true of the fundamentally important experiments of Lamb and Retherford (ZL1) on the fine structure of atomic hydrogen, except that these experiments are not discussed because only molecules of more than one atom are considered relevant to the present discussion.

Since Drude's classical researches, many investigations have been made of the absorption of radio and microwaves in matter. For a long time, however, only very broad resonance bands were found.

Stimulated by Dennison's (ZD5) analysis of the infrared spectra of ammonia, Cleeton and Williams (ZC3) in 1934 discovered the now famous absorption band of ammonia at about 24,000 mc/sec. As discussed in Section 3G, this so-called inversion or "tunneling" spectrum in ammonia arises from transitions between different states which exist by virtue of the possibility of the nitrogen atom going from one side to the other of the plane containing the three hydrogen atoms of NH_3. No other studies of microwave spectroscopy were made until 1945. Then, as discussed in Section 5G, detailed studies of the ammonia spectrum were made by Bleaney and Penrose (ZB8), by Good (G7, C12), and later by a large number of observers (D1, W1, S42, G9, ZW5a, ZX1). These observers found that there were both a fine structure to the spectrum, attributed to the different rotational states of the molecule, and a hyperfine structure due to the electrical quadrupole moment of the molecule. From the fundamental frequency of the spectrum an accurate determination of the frequency of the inversion transition was obtained. From the fine structure of the spectrum, the various rotational parameters of the NH_3 molecule were evaluated. From the hyperfine structure measurements the nuclear quadrupole moment interaction was observed; this interaction has the nuclear interest discussed on page 66 and the molecular interest discussed in Section 5B.

Another quite different variety of microwave spectra is that with O_2, studied by Beringer (ZB5), Townes (ZM2, ZT4a), and others (ZB16). O_2 is one of the relatively few molecules of two or more atoms which is paramagnetic, i.e., which has unpaired electron spins and consequently a large fine structure interaction between the rotational angular momentum and the electronic spin magnetic moment. Beringer's observations in the 5-mm wavelength region corresponded to transitions between two states of different relative orientation of the spin and rotational angular momenta. From the microwave spectrum of $O^{16}O^{17}$, Townes and others (ZM2) have observed a hyperfine structure in the spectrum from which they determine the nature and magnitude of the interaction between the nuclear and electron spins. From this they are able to infer that the unpaired electrons are primarily $2p\pi$ orbits with approximately a 1 percent $2s$ character. The molecular information obtained in these experiments is closely related to that found in the paramagnetic resonance observations of the next section. Consequently, further discussion of it will be deferred until that section. The molecules discussed in the remainder of this section will be assumed to be non-paramagnetic.

The most extensive microwave spectroscopy measurements have been made on spectra arising from rotational transitions, i.e., on spectra which for linear molecules correspond to a change in the rotational quantum number J. The theory of the spectra to be expected in such transitions has been extensively discussed (ZT4a, ZK1a, ZH10, ZH11, G9). For linear molecules the frequencies of the lines in the absence of hyperfine structure should be given by (ZT4a, ZH10, ZK1a)

$$\nu_{J \to J+1} = 2B_v(J + 1) - 4D_J[(J + 1)^3 - (J + 1)l^2] \quad (138)$$

where

$$B_v = \langle h/8\pi^2 I \rangle_v \approx B_e - \Sigma_i \, \alpha_i(v_i + \tfrac{1}{2}d_i) \quad (139)$$

The quantity v_i is the vibrational quantum number of the ith normal mode of vibration, l is the rotational momentum quantum number along the figure axis (zero for diatomic molecules or if $v = 0$), d_i is the degeneracy of the ith vibrational state, and the remaining quantities, such as the centrifugal stretching parameter D_J, are defined by the above relation.

The microwave spectrum of a diatomic molecule like ICl then determines the constants of Eqs. (138) and (139), except for the simplifications of a single mode of vibration and of $l = 0$ and $d_i = 1$ (ZT4a, ZK1a, ZW5, ZT2). From B_e, for example, the mean inverse square of the internuclear spacing can be inferred. Also, experiments, for example, with different Cl isotopes can be used to determine the ratio of the masses of Cl^{37} to Cl^{35}. Recently the possibilities of studying diatomic molecules by the methods of microwave spectroscopy have been markedly extended with the development of high-temperature absorption tubes by Stitch, Honig, and Townes (ZS10) with which such molecules as CsCl and NaCl can be studied.

The frequencies for the pure rotational spectra of linear polyatomic molecules, such as ClCN whose spectrum is shown in Fig. 25, are also given by Eqs. (138) and (139) in the absence of hyperfine structure. Studies with such linear molecules have been particularly effective (ZT4a, ZK1a, G9) as a result of the spectra being easier to interpret than those of the non-linear molecules, and as a result of the spectral lines occurring at experimentally convenient frequencies. From these experiments the molecular quantities of Eq. (138) are determined along with the molecular properties that can be inferred from them.

The theoretical expressions for the pure rotation microwave spectra of symmetric top and asymmetric top molecules are more complicated than Eq. (138), but nevertheless standard (ZT4a, ZK1a, G9, ZH11). An analysis of the pure rotation spectra of such polyatomic molecules determines quantities analogous to those in Eq. (138), including the principal moments of inertia of the molecule. Asymmetric top molecules have been studied by Wilson and others (ZD2, G9, ZK1a, ZX1).

In some polyatomic molecules internal rotation is possible, i.e., one part of the molecule can rotate with respect to another. The theory of such internal rotations in molecules has been developed by Nielsen (ZN1, ZN2), Dennison (ZK5, ZD5), and others. Frequently the internal rotations are not free but are hindered by the potentials of the molecule. Often they require a quantum-mechanical "tunneling" through a potential that is too high for classical particles of that energy to pass over the top. An example of such a hindered rotation in microwave spectroscopy is CH_3OH, which has been studied by Hershberger and Turkevitch (ZH9).

Microwave spectra from free radicals have been observed (ZS2). Lines of sufficient intensity have been obtained with OH radicals to give hope that one may be able to study by microwave methods the OH radicals produced in flames or in other chemical reactions (ZS2).

Hyperfine structure due to nuclear quadrupole moments has been discovered in many microwave spectra and is discussed in greater detail in Section 3G. The significance of these measurements in molecular physics is discussed in Section 5B.

The experiments of Simmons and Gordy (ZS8) showed that, for ammonia, the assumption of nuclear quadrupole coupling alone was not adequate to account for the observed hyperfine structure. Henderson and Van Vleck (ZH7, ZH8) have shown that the discrepancy could be attributed to a spin-rotational interaction of the type discussed in Section 5M. A similar result has been found for FCl (ZG3).

If electric fields are applied to the gas under investigation, the Stark effect on the spectral lines can be observed (ZD1, ZH13, ZT4a, ZX1). Such observations provide experimental data on electric dipole moments of molecules. In addition they frequently simplify the identification of the spectral lines obtained with asymmetric rotators (ZG4). In some cases the variation of electric dipole moment with vibrational state is observed. Thus the dipole moment of OCS in the first excited bending mode of vibration is 0.700 Debye, or about 1.2 percent less than the value of 0.709 Debye for the ground state (ZT4a). (A Debye is 10^{-18} esu.)

Magnetic fields instead of electric fields may also be applied to the molecules. From the resulting Zeeman effect both the nuclear magnetic moments and the molecular rotational magnetic moments can be inferred, as discussed on page 67 and in Section 5N.

In addition to the frequencies, other properties of the microwave spectral lines can be measured as well. One of these is the width of the spectral lines together with a study of the pressure broadening of the lines (ZT4a, ZA2a, ZV1, ZW5, G9, ZN0, ZT1, ZH12c, ZM0a, ZF7). Another is a measurement of the absolute absorption coefficient of the gas (ZB5, G9) as well as a comparison of the experimental value of this coefficient with theory (ZV2, G9). Additional information has been obtained by studying saturation effects in microwave spectroscopy, i.e., the decrease in absorption coefficient and the broadening of the absorption lines that result from the use of excessive microwave power (ZT4a, ZT1, ZB9, ZK1).

The experiments of Hill, Smith, and Howard (ZH12a, ZH12b) on the effects of a foreign gas on the collision broadening of ammonia microwave spectral lines have provided particularly useful molecular information. They (ZH12a, ZH12b) and Anderson (ZA2a) have shown in many cases that the collision broadening is predominantly due to the electric quadrupole moment of the foreign gas molecule (not the nucleus) interacting with the electric dipole moment of ammonia. Consequently, by measuring this broadening when different foreign gases are introduced, they have determined the electric quadrupole moment of the various molecules introduced. In this fashion the electric quadrupole moments of C_2H_2, C_2H_6, NO, HCN, and a number of other molecules have been measured (ZH12a, ZH12b). The significance of results on molecular quadrupole moments is discussed in greater detail in Section 5O.

Extensive summaries of the molecular structure information that has been obtained in microwave studies of the above types have been given in various review articles such as those of Kisliuk, Townes, and Schawlow (ZT4a, ZK1a) in which over 1800 microwave absorption lines are re-

corded and analyzed. The data include the above-described rotation
and rotation-vibration constants such as B_e, α_v, and D_J. From these,
interatomic distances and angles can be inferred. From the Stark effect
experiments, electric dipole moments are obtained. The nuclear quadrupole interactions provide information on the hybridization of bond
types as discussed in Section 5B. The spin-rotational interactions and
the rotational magnetic moment results have the molecular implications
discussed in Sections 5M and 5N. Observations on Λ-type doubling
(V1) have been made with microwaves (ZB6, ZS2, ZX1). Intermediate
varieties of coupling in molecules can be studied including the effects of
both L and S uncoupling (ZT4a).

Numerous measurements of the absorption of microwaves in liquids,
solids, and solutions have also been made. Since several summaries of
these results have been written (ZT6, ZR8), no discussion of the subject
will be given here.

R. Paramagnetic and Ferromagnetic Resonance

Since the magnetic moments of paramagnetic molecules and ions are
about a thousand times larger than nuclear magnetic moments whereas
the electronic and nuclear angular moments are both of the order of h,
the Larmor precession frequencies in paramagnetic materials are about
a thousand times greater than in the nuclear cases discussed on pages
54ff. Consequently, in magnetic fields of a few thousand oersteds the
spectra corresponding to paramagnetic and ferromagnetic resonances
are in the microwave region. These experiments are, therefore, predominantly experiments in microwave spectroscopy for which the
techniques of pages 64ff. are applicable, except that paramagnetic or
ferromagnetic samples are used and external magnetic fields are applied.
Like microwave spectroscopy in the preceding section, the methods of
paramagnetic and ferromagnetic resonance were primarily developed for
studying molecular, ionic, magnetic, and solid state properties, their
applicability to nuclear moment measurements being purely incidental.
As a result, a detailed discussion of the application of these techniques to
molecular, magnetic, and solid state properties is inappropriate here
because their relation to nuclear moments is too unimportant. Consequently, in this section the kinds of applications will be summarized
briefly. For a detailed listing of the results, the reader is referred to
several excellent review articles that have been written on paramagnetic
and ferromagnetic resonance (ZV7, ZG14, ZB11, ZV6).

The first successful paramagnetic resonance experiments were those of
Zavoisky (ZZ1); they were followed shortly by those of Halliday (ZC4),
Bleaney (ZB10), and many others (ZG14, ZV7, ZL2, ZU1, ZX1). A

typical paramagnetic resonance curve is shown in Fig. 36. The nature of such a curve in a single crystal is strongly dependent on the orientation of the crystal relative to the external field and on the degree of magnetic dilution of the crystal. Most of the paramagnetic resonance experiments so far performed have been on salts of the iron (V1) or first

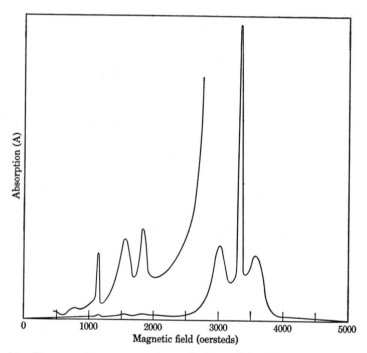

Fig. 36. Paramagnetic resonance for a single crystal of iron ammonium alum, $Fe(NH_4)(SO_4)_2 \cdot 12\ H_2O$. Absorption vs. magnetic field at a magnetic dilution of 1:80 with aluminum alum. Temperature 4.2°K and magnetic field parallel to (1,0,0) directions of the crystal. The two scales differ by a factor of 20 (ZU1).

transition (ZB11) group, i.e., on salts of ions with incomplete $3d$ shells which include suitably ionized Sc, Ti, V, Cr, Mn, Fe, Co, Ni, and Cu.

The simplest paramagnetic resonance to discuss theoretically is that of a free atom or ion. The paramagnetic resonance absorption would occur at the Larmor precession frequency, or, analogously to Eq. (87), at a frequency of $g\mu_0 H_0/h$, where g is the Lande g factor for the atom or ion concerned.

However, in the solid state the electrons of an atom are far from free because they possess electrical charges which are subjected to enormous and, ordinarily, asymmetric electric fields from the surrounding ions. In salts of the iron group, this interaction is so large that the orbital momentum of the electrons ordinarily is almost completely "quenched" (V1). In other words, the torques on the orbital motion due to the electric field are so strong that the orbital magnetic moments, in effect, are reoriented so rapidly in the local fields that they provide no net orbital magnetic moment. The orbital motions of the electrons are then effectively locked to the crystalline electric fields and are uninfluenced by any external magnetic field that can be produced. There remains the magnetic moment associated with spin of the electron which is unaffected except through the influence of the spin-orbit coupling.

The electron spin-orbit coupling admixes some of the orbital magnetic moment with the spin so that the effective g factor (often called the spectroscopic splitting factor in these experiments) is modified and made to depend upon the relative orientation between the magnetic field and the symmetry axes of the crystalline field. A second effect of the spin-orbit interaction is that it tends in part to couple the electron spin to the axes of the crystalline field, so that, if the resultant electron spin S is greater than $\frac{1}{2}$, the energy depends on the orientation of **S** relative to these axes and the $2S + 1$ levels corresponding to different spin orientations are not degenerate even in the absence of an external magnetic field.

With these two effects present, the paramagnetic resonance frequencies can no longer be calculated as simple Larmor frequencies. Instead, by the Bohr relation of Eq. (82), they will be the frequencies, $(E_n - E_m)/h$, corresponding to allowed transitions. The energies E_n should then be calculated from a Hamiltonian which includes spin-orbit effects. A Hamiltonian including the orbital and crystalline field effects in detail would be quite complicated. However, a phenomenological theory suitable for the interpretation of the experiments can be devised (V1, ZB11). This may be done by defining an "effective spin" S by equating the multiplicity of the levels under observation to $2S + 1$. If there is axial symmetry of the crystalline electric field, it is then usually found that the observed spectra can be fitted to a Hamiltonian of the form

$$\mathfrak{H} = g_\parallel \mu_0 H_z S_z + g_\perp \mu_0 (H_x S_x + H_y S_y) + D[S_z{}^2 - \tfrac{1}{3}S(S + 1)] \quad (140)$$

where $g_\parallel$ and $g_\perp$ are the spectroscopic splitting factors for magnetic fields along and perpendicular to the symmetry axis of the electric field. The term in D represents the effect of the above-mentioned coupling of the spin to the crystalline field (ZB14).

Paramagnetic resonance has made an important contribution to the theory of paramagnetism by its experimental determination of the quantities in Eq. (140). Previously such information could be obtained only by the measurement of gross magnetic susceptibilities and anomalous specific heats. These, however, are difficult to interpret, especially when the unit cell of the crystal lattice contains more than one paramagnetic ion and when the crystalline fields for the different ions are differently oriented. Susceptibility measurements give only the net effect of the several ions, whereas in paramagnetic resonance a distinct spectrum is obtained for each ion so that it can be separately investigated. For a summary of the results from paramagnetic resonance studies of the salts of the iron group that are most pertinent to theories of magnetism and the solid state, the reader is referred to a recent review article by Van Vleck (ZV7).

As discussed on page 64, Penrose (P9), Bleaney (B14), and others, by using magnetically dilute crystals, have observed a hyperfine structure in paramagnetic resonance which may be attributed to the nuclear spin. Similar results have been obtained with powders and liquid solutions (ZS4). For example, the spin of vanadium has been confirmed to be $7/2$ in paramagnetic resonance experiments. The hyperfine splitting is due in part to the magnetic interaction between the nuclear and electron spins and in part to nuclear electric quadrupole interaction.

The theory of the hyperfine structure splitting has been developed by Abragam and Pryce (ZA1). Because of the coupling of the electronic orbital motion to the crystalline field and because of the anisotropy of the effective electron magnetic moment, the magnetic hyperfine structure interaction is anisotropic. As it is usually found that there is axial symmetry, the magnetic hyperfine structure interaction contribution can be written as the first two terms of Eq. (141), below. If there is also a quadrupole interaction, it must be added. Finally, the interaction of the nuclear magnetic moment with the external magnetic field must be included; this makes the total addition to the Hamiltonian of Eq. (140) for axial symmetry about the z axis

$$\mathfrak{H}_{\mathrm{hfs}} = AS_z I_z + B(S_x I_x + S_y I_y)$$

$$+ C[I_z^2 - \tfrac{1}{3}I(I+1)] - \hbar\gamma_I \mathbf{I}\cdot\mathbf{H} \quad (141)$$

In the first order the hyperfine structures of the spectral lines are not shifted by the last two terms above, but in higher orders they are because, for example, the quadrupole interaction tries to align the nuclei one way while the magnetic field from the electrons tries to align them in a different direction, so the quadrupole interaction energy is altered when the electron spins are reoriented. By a comparison of theory and experiment both the magnetic interaction between the nucleus and the electron and the quadrupole interaction can be measured. The non-nuclear significance of the latter is discussed in Section 5C.

In addition to experiments with the salts of the iron group, a limited number of paramagnetic resonance measurements have been made on the rare earths, mainly the ethyl sulfates thereof (B14b, ZE1). Hyperfine structure has been found in the paramagnetic resonance experiments with rare earths. Several spins including Nd^{143} and Nd^{145} have been measured for the first time this way (B14b). Results of such measurements are included in the tables of Section 4.

Paramagnetic resonance has also been detected in x-ray-induced color centers of lithium fluoride, potassium chloride, sodium chloride, and other crystals by Hutchinson (ZH16) and others (ZS4) at concentrations of 10^{17} per cm^3 with a resonance width of about 40 gauss. The paramagnetic resonance of Mn^{++} ions in Mn-activated ZnS phosphors has been observed (ZS4). Paramagnetic resonance has also been detected with organic radicals (ZS2, ZT4a) and metal ammonium solutions (ZH16).

Recently, Griswold, Kip, and Kittel (ZG9) have succeeded in detecting the paramagnetic resonance of semi-conductors and of the conduction electrons in metals. This technique may prove valuable in investigations of the theories of semi-conductors and conductors.

A variety of paramagnetic resonance experiment that has been of value to molecular rather than solid state theory has been the study of paramagnetic molecules such as O_2, NO, NO_2, and ClO_2 (ZB6, ZM1a, ZT4a). Beringer (ZB6), for example, with NO has observed the hyperfine structure due to the magnetic interaction of the nucleus and the electron. These experiments and the significance of their results are closely related to the O_2 experiments in the absence of an external magnetic field, discussed in the preceding section.

So far in this section we have discussed only the information that is obtainable from measurements of the proper frequency of the paramagnetic resonance lines. From the study of the line widths, considerable information is obtained concerning the exchange forces between ions. As discussed by Van Vleck and Gorter (ZG7, ZV3), the phenomenon of "exchange narrowing" as in Section 5G makes the lines in a paramagnetic substance with isotropic g factors much narrower than they would be otherwise. On the other hand, when the g factors are anisotropic, the exchange forces may tend to blur together lines which would otherwise be distinct isolated lines, and so these forces have a widening action (ZV3, ZB1, ZP10).

Ferromagnetic resonance absorption was theoretically discussed as early as 1921 (ZG1, ZL3), but it was first observed by Griffiths (ZG8) in 1946 and has been studied by Kittel (ZK3, ZK4) and a number of others (ZK2, ZY1). In a typical experiment the ferromagnetic sample forms all or part of one end of a cavity resonator, so that the oscillatory magnetic field from the microwaves in the cavity is parallel to the wall. A fixed magnetic field is applied parallel to the same wall but perpendicular to the oscillatory field. The effective Q of the cavity is then measured. Since the energy lost by a high-frequency current in a magnetic conductor is proportional to the product of the resistivity ρ and the permeability μ, the value of μ can be inferred from the cavity Q. The measurement of the effective μ in this fashion is then carried out as a function of the external magnetic field H. A marked resonance variation is indeed found as shown in Fig. 37. However, the ferromagnetic resonance occurs both with an excessive width and at an applied magnetic field H that is several times smaller than that of the Larmor formula.

Kittel (ZK3) pointed out that in ferromagnetic resonance the demagnetizing effects are large and must be included. Since near resonance, by Eq. (113), the magnetization has appreciable components normal to H, demagnetization factors for fields in these directions must be included as well; this makes the demagnetization calculation much more complicated than in the static case. However, by a relatively simple macroscopic calculation related to that on page 57, Kittel (ZK3, ZV4) derived an expression for the resonance frequency that depended on the shape of the region into which the alternating magnetic field penetrated. For the resonant cavity with a ferromagnetic wall described previously, Kittel's formula for the resonance frequency reduces to

$$\nu = \frac{ge}{4\pi mc}\sqrt{HB} \tag{142}$$

where g is the spectroscopic splitting factor as used in the preceding section and where corrections for anisotropy have been omitted. With this formula, agreement between theory and experiment could be achieved with a g of about 2.1. Furthermore, the effects of shape, the anisotropy corrections, and the forms of resonance curves predicted by the general theory are in agreement with experiment (ZK2, ZB13), as shown in Fig. 37 where the plotted curve is the theoretical one with $g = 2.17$ for Supermalloy and with an assumed relaxation time to give the best fit. Reproducible results can be obtained in these experiments only with carefully annealed and strain-free samples.

On the other hand, the ferromagnetic resonance curves are broader than they should be and the breadth does not decrease with temperature as much as would be expected; in other words, the relaxation time to give the excellent agreement of Fig. 37 is experimentally smaller than expected theoretically (ZB13). An adequate explanation is required. Another difficulty is that the spectroscopic splitting factors g that must

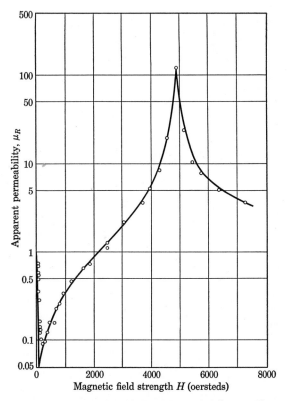

Fig. 37. Ferromagnetic resonance absorption in annealed Supermalloy at 23,900 mc. The ordinate is on a logarithmic scale, making the resonance less conspicuous. The full curve shows the theoretical variation on the basis of Kittel's theory when the relaxation constant is chosen to give the best fit (ZY1).

be assumed to make Eq. (142) agree with experiment are too high, being approximately 2.2 for iron, cobalt, and nickel. Kittel (ZK3) and Van Vleck (ZV5) have shown that the spectroscopic splitting factor g can indeed depart from 2 (or more exactly, by page 51, from 2×1.00115) as a result of spin-orbit coupling and the crystalline electric field. However, if it does, they show that the gyromagnetic ratio g', determined by experiments like that of Einstein-deHaas, should depart from 2 by the same amount but in the opposite direction. That is, the following relation should apply:

$$g - 2 = 2 - g' \qquad (143)$$

Since g' for the above metals is about 1.9, Eq. (143) is violated.

Resonance experiments with anti-ferromagnetic materials have been performed (ZT5, ZV6, ZP5, ZU1a, ZK4a). In these it is found that for H in one crystalline direction a paramagnetic resonance absorption which is strong above the Curie temperature drops very abruptly at the Curie temperature. With $CuCl_2 \cdot 2H_2O$ at low temperatures an additional anti-ferromagnetic resonance band for H in a different direction has been observed which disappears at higher temperatures (ZP5, ZU1a).

APPENDIX

A. Nuclear Shell Structure

Although for many nuclear physics calculations a model of the nucleus analogous to a liquid drop seems most suitable (ZW6), there is nevertheless also strong empirical evidence for some form of shell structure in nuclei. In particular there is now abundant evidence that certain special numbers of neutrons or of protons in a nucleus form particularly stable configurations even in heavy nuclei, as was first pointed out by Elsasser (ZE1a) and as emphasized by Mayer (M11), Jensen, Haxel, and Suess (ZJ4, ZJ5), and others (ZW8, ZF2, ZB2, ZB7, ZC2, ZL6, ZH14, ZW4). The so-called magic numbers for which there is special stability are 2, 8, 20, 50, 82, and 126. The evidence for the lowest numbers is well known and is well illustrated by the high stability of He^4 and O^{16}. However, the evidence for the larger numbers is also strong. Thus, of the three isotopes with even $Z > 32$ and with more than 60 percent relative abundance in their respective elements, two have 82 neutrons and one has 50 neutrons. Also the elements with the unusually large numbers of isotopes and with the largest difference of mass number between the heaviest and the lightest isotope are those with 20, 50, or 82 protons. Similarly lead with $Z = 82$ is the end of all heavy natural radioactive chains, and its heaviest isotope has 126 neutrons. Energies of radioactive decay products show that the binding of neutrons in a nucleus has a 2.2-Mev discontinuity at 126 neutrons and the proton binding energy has a discontinuity of 1.6 Mev at 82 protons. Furthermore nuclei with 50 or 82 of either protons or neutrons are particularly abundant in the earth. Two of the rare identified delayed neutron emitters are Kr^{87} and Xe^{137}, which have 51 and 83 neutrons, respectively, consistent with the last neutron beyond 50 or 82 being relatively weakly bound. Again, the neutron absorption cross sections for nuclei containing 50, 80, or 126 neutrons are unusually low. The occurrence of nuclear isomerism can be correlated with the magic numbers (ZA6, ZH12, ZG5). Finally some of the most conspicuous disagreements between the experimental nuclear masses and the semi-empirical formula can be accounted for if nuclei of 50 and 82 neutrons are assumed to be particularly stable.

This result implies that there is some form of shell structure in a nucleus. Further evidence for such a shell structure was described in Section 4, where it was pointed out that isotopes differing by just 2 neutrons often have almost exactly the same magnetic moments as if the 2 neutrons just canceled each other's effect, as would be more reasonable from a shell model point of view than from that of a liquid drop. The success of the Schmidt model in nuclear moment theory also lends support to a shell structure theory of nuclei.

It is somewhat surprising that a shell structure should exist in heavy nuclei because the interaction between neighboring nuclear particles should be very strong indeed. It may be made possible, however, by the neighboring nuclear potentials blending together to form a roughly uniform potential and by virtue of the nuclear system being highly degenerate so that the Pauli exclusion principle reduces the probability of nucleon collisions (ZW6).

The high stability of a system with 2, 8, or 20 like nucleons can easily be accounted for if the nucleons are assumed to move approximately independently in a square well potential. For example, 20 like nucleons would correspond to two $1s$, six $1p$, ten $1d$, and two $2s$ like nucleons. However, the high stability of 50, 82, and 126 does not follow immediately from such a simple model. Feenberg (F5, ZF3, ZF4), Nordheim (ZN3, ZF4), Mayer (M11), and Jensen, Haxel, and Suess (ZJ5) have shown that the mean potential throughout the nucleus can be modified in various ways to produce the magic numbers. Thus Feenberg shows that this can be accomplished if the mean potential well is deeper at the edges than at the middle, whereas Mayer (M11, ZG2) and Jensen, Haxel, and Suess (ZJ5) have accomplished a similar result by a single-particle picture with an assumed strong spin orbital coupling.

How a suitable spin orbital coupling can accomplish this can be seen with the aid of Fig. 38 as follows. With an independent-particle model in which each nucleon is assumed to move in the mean potential of the nucleus unaffected by the location of other nucleons, one can calculate the allowed energies of the nucleons for different assumed mean potentials inside the nucleus. For two forms of this potential the calculations are particularly simple. One of these is a simple three-dimensional square well potential of infinite depth for which the radial eigenfunctions are Bessel functions (ZS3). The energy eigenvalues for such a system can readily be calculated (ZS3, ZJ5) and are plotted on the right side of Fig. 38 along with the designation of the state, the number $(2[2l + 1])$ of like nucleons that can exist in each shell in accordance with the Pauli principle, and the accumulated number of particles at, or below, the energy of the state. The accumulated numbers are in parentheses. Another potential for which calculations are simple (ZS3, ZJ5) is the simple harmonic oscillator potential for which the allowed energies and corresponding numbers are plotted on the left side of Fig. 38. The shape of the actual mean nuclear well is probably some-

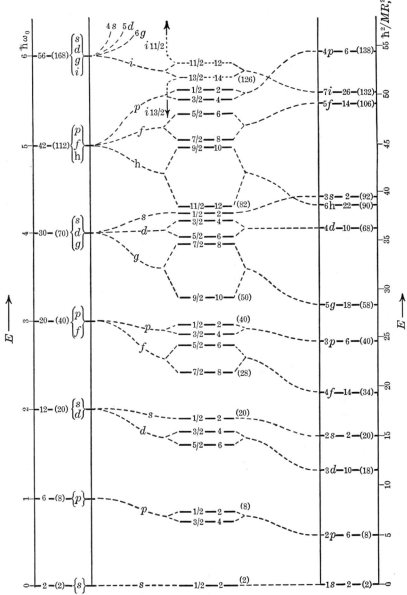

Fig. 38. Nuclear shells. The energy levels of an infinitely deep rectangular well are shown on the right, and those of a simple harmonic oscillator potential on the left. The numbers in parentheses are the accumulated number of electrons in that shell or lower. The levels in the center are at energies intermediate between those of the square well potential and the simple harmonic oscillator potential. In addition a strong spin orbital interaction is assumed for these levels (ZJ5).

what intermediate between each of the above two models, as is indicated by the interconnection of the corresponding states of the two models by dotted lines. The above postulates alone, however, are not sufficient to give all the magic numbers. Mayer (M11) and Jensen, Haxel, and Suess (ZJ5) independently pointed out that the magic numbers would be produced if one assumed the existence of a strong spin orbital interaction such that the larger j is lower in energy. From Fig. 38 it is immediately apparent that such a splitting of levels of different j can give the magic numbers.

With the aid of suitable rules for the coupling of the different nucleon angular momenta, one can calculate nuclear spins and magnetic moments from the above model. If either the number of neutrons or the number of protons is even, Mayer (M11) and Jensen, Haxel, and Suess (ZJ5) give the coupling rule that an even number of like nucleons in a shell have their angular momenta just compensate, and an odd number of like nucleons in a shell add up to the angular momentum of a single nucleon in the shell. Thus, for $_{49}\text{In}^{113}$, there are 64 neutrons and 49 protons, so that from Fig. 38 all shells are closed except for a $g_{9/2}$ shell; therefore the spin should be $9/2$, as it is experimentally. If both the number of neutrons and the number of protons are odd, Nordheim (ZN3) proposes the coupling rule that, if the spin and orbital angular momenta for one kind of nucleon are parallel while they are anti-parallel for the other kind of nucleon, the nuclear spin is small, i.e., close to the difference in the j's of the two kinds of nucleons, while the resultant nuclear spin is close to the sum of the j's if the spins and orbital angular momenta of the two types of nucleons are similarly coupled (both parallel or both anti-parallel). These coupling rules are not completely inviolate.

For nuclei whose total number of nucleons is odd, the above model provides a means for calculating the nuclear magnetic moment. By the above rules, one need consider only the odd nucleon, and its spin and orbital magnetic moment can be combined by a procedure similar to that in calculating the Lande g factor. Let $\mathbf{\mu}_I$ be the magnetic moment vector when the nucleus is in an orientation state with $m = I$ relative to a unit vector $\mathbf{k}$, and let g_L and g_S be the orbital and spin g factors of the nucleon. Then the nuclear moment with the aid of Eq. (15) of Section 2 is

$$\mu = \mathbf{\mu}_I \cdot \mathbf{k} = [\mu_{NM}(g_L \mathbf{L} + g_S \mathbf{S}) \cdot \mathbf{I} \mathbf{I} \cdot \mathbf{k}]/\mathbf{I} \cdot \mathbf{I}$$

$$= g_L \mu_{NM} \frac{I(I+1) + L(L+1) - S(S+1)}{2(I+1)} \tag{144}$$

$$+ g_S \mu_{NM} \frac{I(I+1) + S(S+1) - L(L+1)}{2(I+1)}$$

Since S is $\frac{1}{2}$, $I = L \pm \frac{1}{2}$, one can eliminate S and L in Eq. (144) to obtain the relations

$$\mu = (I - \tfrac{1}{2})g_L\mu_{NM} + \tfrac{1}{2}g_S\mu_{NM} \qquad (145)$$

for $I = L + \frac{1}{2}$, and

$$\mu = \frac{I^2 + \tfrac{3}{2}I}{I + 1}\,g_L\mu_{NM} - \frac{1}{2}\frac{I}{I + 1}\,g_S\mu_{NM} \qquad (146)$$

for $I = L - \frac{1}{2}$. When g_L is given the value 1 for protons and 0 for neutrons while g_S is given the value 5.58 for protons and -3.83 for neutrons, Eqs. (145) and (146) just give the equations of the Schmidt lines of Figs. 28 and 29.

Extensive applications of the nuclear shell principles to specific nuclei have been given in two recent review articles by Klinkenberg (Z6) and Goldhaber (ZG6).

REFERENCES

Those references which relate to the value of a specific nuclear moment have the element and the method of measurement indicated in parentheses after the reference. The symbols preceding the dash (–) in the parentheses indicate the element; those following the dash indicate the method of observation according to the following convention:

A   atomic beam magnetic resonance
B   band spectra
C   Raman spectra
D   nature of radioactive decay
H   specific heat
M   molecular beam magnetic resonance
N   nuclear scattering
O   ortho-para conversion
P   polarization of resonance radiation
R   nuclear resonance absorption or induction
S   hyperfine structure in line spectra
W   microwave absorption
Z   zero moment or atomic beam deflection

Because some of the references were prepared later than others, there is a double alphabetical listing, the references added later being preceded by Z.

(A1)   L. W. Alvarez and F. Bloch, Phys. Rev., **57**, 111 (1940). (*n*–A)
(A1a)   F. Alder and F. C. Yu, Phys. Rev., **81**, 1067 (1951); **82**, 105 (1951).
        (O, Mg, Re, Bc–R)
(A2)   N. I. Adams, M.I.T. Research Laboratory of Electronics Report (October
        1949), p. 24; N. I. Adams and T. F. Wimett, *ibid*. (B, Rb–R)
(A2a)   E. N. Adams, Phys. Rev., **81**, 1 (1951).
(A3)   D. A. Anderson, Phys. Rev., **76**, 434 (1949). (B–R)
(A4)   H. L. Anderson and A. Novick, Phys. Rev., **71**, 372 (1947). (H–R)
(A5)   H. L. Anderson and A. Novick, Phys. Rev., **73**, 919 (1948); H. L. Anderson,
        Phys. Rev., **45**, 1460 (1949). (He–R)
(A6)   O. E. Anderson, Phys. Rev., **45**, 685 (1934). (La–S)
(A7)   O. E. Anderson and H. E. White, Phys. Rev., **71**, 911 (1947). (U–S)
(A8)   W. R. Arnold and A. Roberts, Phys. Rev., **71**, 878 (1947). (*n*, H–R)
(A9)   O. H. Arroe, Phys. Rev., **74**, 1263 (1948). (Zn–S)
(A10)   O. H. Arroe and J. E. Mack, Phys. Rev., **76**, 873 (1949). (Zr–S)
(A11)   O. H. Arroe, Phys. Rev., **77**, 745A (1950). (Ba–S)
(A12)   O. H. Arroe, Phys. Rev., **77**, 745 (1950). (Ba–S)
(A13)   O. H. Arroe, unpublished work and Phys. Rev., **79**, 836 (1950). (Ni, Ba–S)
(A13a) Altshuler, Kozyrev, and Salikhov, Dokl. Akad. Nauk, S.S.S.R., **71**, 855
        (1950).
(A14)   R. Avery and C. H. Blanchard, Phys. Rev., **78**, 704 (1950).
(B1)   R. F. Bacher and D. H. Tomboulian, Phys. Rev., **52**, 836 (1937). (In–S)
(B2)   J. S. Badami, Z. Physik, **79**, 206 (1932); **79**, 224 (1932). (Sb–S)
(B3)   S. S. Ballard, Phys. Rev., **46**, 806 (1934). (Nb–S)

(B4)   J. Bardeen and C. H. Townes, Phys. Rev., **73**, 97 (1948).

(B4a) G. Becker and H. Krüger, Naturwiss., **38**, 121 (1951).

(B4b) J. C. Bellamy, Nature, **168**, 556 (1951).

(B5)   G. E. Becker and P. Kusch, Phys. Rev., **73**, 584 (1948).   (Ga–A)

(B5a) G. J. Bené, P. M. Denis, and R. C. Extermann, Physica, **17**, 303 (1951).

(B6)   H. Bethe, Phys. Rev., **53**, 842 (1938).

(B7)   Berman, Kusch, and Mann, Phys. Rev., **77**, 140 (1950).   (Tl–A)

(B8)   R. Birge, Phys. Rev., **79**, 194 (1950).

(B9)   Bitter, Alpert, Nagle, and Poss, Phys. Rev., **72**, 1271 (1947).   (H–R)

(B10) F. Bitter, Phys. Rev., **75**, 1326A (1949); **76**, 150 (1949).
       (Li, B, Na, Al, P, Cl, Cu, Br, Rb, Cs–R)

(B11) F. Bitter, Phys. Rev., **76**, 150 (1949).

(B12) F. Bitter, unpublished work.   (H–R)

(B13) F. Bitter, Phys. Rev., **76**, 833 (1949).

(B14) Bleaney, Ingram, and Pryce, Nature, **164**, 116 (1949); Proc. Phys. Soc.
       (London), **A63**, 1369 (1950); Proc. Roy. Soc. (London), **A205**, 135 (1951).

(B14a) B. Bleaney, K. Bowers, and D. J. Ingram, Proc. Phys. Soc., **A64**, 785 (1951).

(B14b) B. Bleaney and H. E. D. Scovil, Proc. Phys. Soc., **A64**, 204 and 601 (1951)
       and **A63**, 1369 (1950).

(B14c) B. Bleaney and D. J. Ingram, Proc. Roy. Soc., **A205**, 336 (1951).

(B14d) B. Bleaney, Proc. Phys. Soc., **A64**, 315 (1951) and Phil. Mag., **42**, 411 (1951).

(B15) F. Bloch, Phys. Rev., **50**, 259 (1936); **51**, 994 (1937).

(B16) F. Bloch and Siegert, Phys. Rev., **57**, 522 (1940).

(B17) Bloch, Hammermesh, and Staub, Phys. Rev., **64**, 47 (1943).

(B18) Bloch, Hansen, and Packard, Phys. Rev., **69**, 127 (1946); **70**, 474 (1946).

(B19) Bloch, Condit, and Staub, Phys. Rev., **70**, 927 (1946).

(B20) F. Bloch, Phys. Rev., **70**, 460 (1946); **89**, 728 (1953).

(B21) Bloch, Graves, Packard, and Spence, Phys. Rev., **71**, 373 (1947).   (H–R)

(B22) Bloch, Graves, Packard, and Spence, Phys. Rev., **71**, 551 (1947).   (H–R)

(B23) Bloch, Levinthal, and Packard, Phys. Rev., **72**, 1125 (1947).   (H–R)

(B24) Bloch, Nicodemus, and Staub, Phys. Rev., **74**, 1025 (1948).   (n–R)

(B25) F. Bloch and C. D. Jeffries, Phys. Rev., **80**, 305 (1950).

(B25a) F. Bloch, Phys. Rev., **83**, 839 (1951).

(B26) Bloembergen, Purcell, and Pound, Phys. Rev., **73**, 679 (1948).

(B27) N. Bloembergen and W. Dickinson, Phys. Rev., **79**, 179 (1950).

(B28) A. Bohr, Phys. Rev., **73**, 1109 (1948).

(B29) A. Bohr and V. Weisskopf, Phys. Rev., **77**, 94 (1950).

(B30) A. Bohr, private communication.

(B30a) A. Bohr, Phys. Rev., **81**, 134 and 331 (1951).

(B31) S. Borowitz and W. Kohn, Phys. Rev., **76**, 818 (1949).

(B32) G. Breit, Nature, **122**, 649 (1928).

(B33) J. K. Bragg, Phys. Rev., **74**, 533 (1948).

(B34) G. Breit, Phys. Rev., **35**, 1447 (1930).

(B35) G. Breit and I. Rabi, Phys. Rev., **38**, 2082 (1931).

(B36) G. Breit and J. Rosenthal, Phys. Rev., **42**, 348 (1932); **41**, 459 (1932).

(B37) G. Breit and L. Wills, Phys. Rev., **44**, 470 (1933).

(B38) G. Breit, Phys. Rev., **72**, 984 (1947).

(B39) G. Breit and F. Bloch, Phys. Rev., **72**, 135 (1947).

(B40) G. Breit and R. E. Meyerott, Phys. Rev., **72**, 1023 (1947); **75**, 1447 (1949).

(B41) G. Breit and G. E. Brown, Phys. Rev., **74**, 1278 (1948).

(B42)   Breit, Brown, and Arfken, Phys. Rev., **76**, 1299 (1949).

(B43)   G. Breit, Phys. Rev., **78**, 390, 470 (1950); **77**, 568 (1950); **79**, 891 (1950).

(B44)   P. Brix and H. Kopfermann, Z. Physik, **126**, 344 (1949); Naturwiss., **37**, 397 (1950) and Göttingen Nach., **2**, 31 (1947). (Sm, Ir–S)

(B45)   P. Brix, Z. Physik, **126**, 725 (1949). (Cu–S)

(B46)   Brody, Nierenberg, and Ramsey, Phys. Rev., **72**, 258 (1947). (Br–M)

(B47)   H. Brooks, Phys. Rev., **59**, 925 (1941); **60**, 168 (1941).

(B48)   J. Brossel, Phys. Rev., **76**, 858 (1949).

(B49)   T. L. de Bruin, Nature, **125**, 414 (1930).

(C1)   J. S. Campbell, Phys. Rev., **40**, 1040A (1932); Nature, **131**, 204 (1933). (Ga, In–S)

(C2)   J. S. Campbell, Z. Physik, **84**, 393 (1933). (F, Br–S)

(C3)   K. M. Case, Phys. Rev., **76**, 1 (1949).

(C4)   H. Casimir, Z. Physik, **77**, 811 (1932).

(C5)   H. Casimir, Physica, **2**, 719 (1935). (Lu–S)

(C6)   H. B. G. Casimir, *On the Interaction Between Atomic Nuclei and Electrons*, Teylers Tweede Genootschop, Haarlem, Holland.

(C7)   H. Casimir, Physica, **7**, 169 (1940).

(C8)   H. B. G. Casimir and G. Karreman, Physica, **9**, 494 (1942).

(C9)   W. H. Chambers and D. Williams, Phys. Rev., **76**, 638 (1949). (Be, P, Cl, Rb, Co, La–R)

(C10)   Chambers, Sheriff, and Williams, tentative value from unpublished work and Phys. Rev., **83**, 858 (1951). (Mn–R)

(C11)   V. W. Cohen, Phys. Rev., **46**, 713 (1934). (Cs–Z)

(C12)   D. K. Coles and W. E. Good, Phys. Rev., **70**, 979 (1946).

(C13)   Cohen, Koski, and Wentink, Phys. Rev., **76**, 703 (1949). (S–W)

(C14)   Cohen, Koski, and Wentink, Phys. Rev., **77**, 742A (1950). (S–R)

(C15)   Cohen, Knight, Wentink, and Koski, Phys. Rev., **79**, 191 (1950). (Sb–R)

(C16)   E. U. Condon and G. H. Shortley, *Theory of Atomic Spectra*, Cambridge University Press, 1935.

(C17)   M. F. Crawford and A. M. Crooker, Nature, **131**, 655 (1933). (As–S)

(C18)   M. F. Crawford and S. Bateson, Can. J. Research, **A10**, 693 (1934). (Sb–S)

(C19)   Crawford, Schawlow, Gray, and Kelly, Phys. Rev., **75**, 1112 (1949). (Ag–S)

(C20)   M. F. Crawford and A. L. Schawlow, Phys. Rev., **76**, 1310 (1949). (Te, Pb–S)

(C21)   Crawford, Kelly, Schawlow, and Gray, Phys. Rev., **76**, 1527 (1949) and Can. J. Research, **A28**, 558 (1950). (Mg–S)

(C22)   M. F. Crawford and N. Olson, Phys. Rev., **76**, 1528 (1949). (Y–S)

(C23)   M. F. Crawford and J. Levinson, Can. J. Research, **A27**, 156 (1949). (P–S)

(C24)   M. F. Crawford, private communication. (Mg–S)

(C25)   A. M. Crooker, Can. J. Research, **A14**, 115 (1936). (Pb–S)

(D1)   Dailey, Kyhl, Strandberg, Van Vleck, and Wilson, Phys. Rev., **70**, 984 (1946). (N–W)

(D2)   Dailey, Rusinow, Shulman, and Townes, Phys. Rev., **74**, 1245A (1948). (As–W)

(D2a)   J. M. Daniels, M. A. Grace, and F. N. H. Robinson, Nature, **168**, 781 (1951).

(D3)   L. Davis, Phys. Rev., **74**, 1193 (1948). (Na–A)

(D4)   L. Davis and C. W. Zabel, Phys. Rev., **74**, 1211A (1948). (Cl–A)

(D5)   L. Davis, Phys. Rev., **76**, 435 (1949). (Cs–A)

(D6)   Davis, Nagle, and Zacharias, Phys. Rev., **76**, 1068 (1949). (Na, K, Cs–A)

References 145

(D7)   Davis, Feld, Zabel, and Zacharias, Phys. Rev., **76**, 1076 (1949). (Al, Cl, Ga, In–A)

(D7a)   A. De Shalit, Helv. Phys. Acta, **24**, 296 (1951) and Phys. Rev., **80**, 103 (1950).

(D8)   H. G. Dehmelt and H. Krüger, Naturwiss., **37**, 111 (1950); Zeits. Phys., **129**, 401 (1951); H. G. Dehmelt, Naturwiss., **37**, 398 (1950).

(D9)   D. M. Dennison, Proc. Roy. Soc. (London), **A115**, 483 (1927). (H–H)

(D9a)   S. S. Dharmatti and H. E. Weaver, Phys. Rev., **83**, 845 (1951); **84**, 843 (1951) and **84**, 367 (1951).

(D10)   W. C. Dickinson and T. F. Wimett, Phys. Rev., **75**, 1769 (1949). (Be–R)

(D11)   W. C. Dickinson, Phys. Rev., **76**, 1414 (1949). (La–R)

(D12)   W. Dickinson, Phys. Rev., **77**, 736 (1950).

(D13)   W. Dickinson, private communication.

(D14)   G. H. Dieke and F. S. Tomkins, Phys. Rev., **76**, 283 (1949). (H–B)

(D15)   A. E. Douglas and G. Herzberg, Phys. Rev., **76**, 1529 (1949). (He–B)

(D16)   S. D. Drell, Phys. Rev., **76**, 427 (1949).

(D17)   J. W. M. DuMond and E. R. Cohen, Phys. Rev., **77**, 411 (1950); Phys. Rev., **82**, 556 (1951).

(E1)   A. Ellett and N. P. Heydenburg, Phys. Rev., **46**, 583 (1934); L. Larrick, Phys. Rev., **46**, 581 (1934). (Na–P)

(E2)   R. M. Elliott and J. Wulff, Phys. Rev., **55**, 170 (1939). (Au–S)

(E3)   I. Estermann and O. Stern, Z. Physik, **85**, 17 (1933).

(E4)   Estermann, Simpson, and Stern, Phys. Rev., **52**, 535 (1937).

(E5)   I. Estermann, Rev. Mod. Phys., **18**, 300 (1946).

(F1)   Farkas, Farkas, and Harteck, Proc. Roy. Soc. (London), **A144**, 481 (1934). (H–O)

(F2)   A. Farkas and U. Garbatski, J. Chem. Phys., **6**, 260 (1938).

(F3)   Farkas and Sandler, Trans. Faraday Soc., **35**, 337 (1939).

(F4)   E. Feenberg and E. Wigner, Phys. Rev., **51**, 95 (1937).

(F5)   E. Feenberg and K. C. Hammack, Phys. Rev., **75**, 1877 (1949).

(F6)   B. Feld and W. Lamb, Phys. Rev., **67**, 15 (1945).

(F7)   B. T. Feld, Phys. Rev., **72**, 1116 (1947).

(F8)   E. Fermi, Z. Physik, **60**, 320 (1930).

(F9)   E. Fermi and E. Segrè, Z. Physik, **82**, 729 (1933).

(F9a)   M. Fierz, Göttingen Nach., **3**, 1 (1947).

(F10)   R. A. Fisher and E. R. Peck, Phys. Rev., **55**, 270 (1939). (Mn–S)

(F10a) L. L. Foldy and F. J. Milford, Phys. Rev., **80**, 751 (1950).

(F11)   H. Foley, Phys. Rev., **71**, 747 (1947).

(F12)   H. Foley, Phys. Rev., **80**, 288 (1950).

(F13)   T. Folsche, Z. Physik, **105**, 133 (1937). (Cs–S)

(F14)   G. R. Fowles, Phys. Rev., **76**, 571 (1949). (Te–S)

(F15)   G. R. Fowles, Phys. Rev., **78**, 744 (1950). (Te, W–S)

(F16)   M. Fox and I. I. Rabi, Phys. Rev., **48**, 746 (1935). (Li, Na, K–Z)

(F17)   R. Fraser, *Molecular Rays*, Cambridge University Press, 1931.

(F18)   R. Fraser, *Molecular Beams*, Methuen & Co., Ltd., London, 1937.

(F19)   H. T. Friis, Proc. Inst. Radio Engrs., **32**, 419 (1944).

(F20)   S. Frisch, Z. Physik, **71**, 89 (1931). (Ca, Sr–S)

(F21)   R. Frisch and O. Stern, Z. Physik, **85**, 4 (1933).

(F21a) O. Frisch, private communication.

(F22)   Fröhlich, Heitler, and Kemmer, Proc. Roy. Soc. (London), **A166**, 154 (1938).

146 References

(F23) B. Fuchs and H. Kopfermann, Naturwiss., **23**, 372 (1935). (Pt–S)

(G1) H. G. Gale and G. S. Monk, Astrophys. J., **69**, 77 (1929). (F–B)

(G2) J. H. Gardner and E. M. Purcell, Phys. Rev., **76**, 1262 (1949) and **83**, 996 (1951). (H–R)

(G3) F. E. Geiger, unpublished work. (Pb–S)

(G4) C. Gerthsen, Ann. Physik, **9**, 769 (1931); Physik. Z., **38**, 833 (1937).

(G4a) S. Geschwind, R. Gunther-Mohr, and C. H. Townes, Phys. Rev., **81**, 288 (1951) and **83**, 208 (1951).

(G5) J. H. Gisolf and P. Zeeman, Nature, **132**, 566 (1933); J. H. Gisolf, dissertation, Amsterdam, 1935. (Ta–S)

(G6) H. Gollnow, Z. Physik, **103**, 443 (1936). (Lu–S)

(G7) W. E. Good, Phys. Rev., **69**, 539 (1946); **70**, 213 (1946).

(G8) Gordy, Smith, and Simmons, Phys. Rev., **72**, 249 (1947); Gordy, Smith, Smith, and Ring, Phys. Rev., **72**, 259 (1947); **74**, 243 (1948); **74**, 370 (1948). (Br, I, Cl–W)

(G9) Gordy, Smith, and Trambarulo, *Microwave Spectroscopy*, John Wiley & Sons, New York (1953); W. Gordy, Revs. Mod. Phys., **20**, 668 (1948); Gordy, Gilliam, and Livingston, Phys. Rev., **76**, 443 (1949). (F, Cl, Br, I–W)

(G10) Gordy, Ring, and Burg, Phys. Rev., **74**, 1191 (1948); erratum, **75**, 208 (1949); **75**, 1325A (1949); W. Gordy, Phys. Rev., **76**, 139 (1949). (B–W)

(G11) W. Gordy, Phys. Rev., **76**, 139 (1949).

(G12) Gordy, Ring, and Burg, Phys. Rev., **78**, 512 (1950). (B–W)

(G13) W. Gordy and R. Anderson, unpublished work. (Se–W)

(G14) C. J. Gorter, Physica, **3**, 503, 995 (1936).

(G15) C. J. Gorter and L. J. F. Broer, Physica, **9**, 591 (1942).

(G15a) C. J. Gorter, Physica, **14**, 504 (1948).

(G15b) C. J. Gorter, D. de Klerk, O. J. Poppema, M. J. Steenland, H. de Vries, Physica, **15**, 679 (1949).

(G16) S. Goudsmit and E. Back, Z. Physik, **43**, 321 (1927); E. Back and S. Goudsmit, Z. Physik, **47**, 174 (1928). (Bi–S)

(G17) S. Goudsmit and R. Bacher, Phys. Rev., **34**, 1499 (1929).

(G18) S. Goudsmit, Phys. Rev., **37**, 663 (1931).

(G19) S. Goudsmit, Phys. Rev., **43**, 636 (1933).

(G20) S. Goudsmit and R. Bacher, Phys. Rev., **43**, 894 (1933).

(G21) S. Goudsmit, Phys. Rev., **43**, 636 (1933).
       (Cu, Ga, As, Cd, Sb, Hg, Tl, Pb, Bi–S)

(G22) N. S. Grace, Phys. Rev., **43**, 762 (1933). (Co–S)

(G23) N. S. Grace and E. MacMillan, Phys. Rev., **44**, 325A (1933); E. MacMillan and N. S. Grace, Phys. Rev., **44**, 949 (1933a). (T–S)

(G24) N. S. Grace and K. R. More, Phys. Rev., **45**, 166 (1934). (Cr, Mo, W–S)

(G25) L. P. Granath, Phys. Rev., **36**, 1018 (1930). (Li–S)

(G26) L. P. Granath, Phys. Rev., **42**, 44 (1932). (Li–S)

(G27) L. P. Granath and C. M. Van Atta, Phys. Rev., **44**, 935 (1933). (Li–S)

(G28) W. Gremmer and R. Ritschl, Z. Instrumentenk., **51**, 170 (1930). (Re–S)

(G29) P. Güttinger and W. Pauli, Z. Physik, **67**, 743 (1931). (Li–S)

(G30) M. Gurevitch, Phys. Rev., **75**, 767 (1949). (Sn–S)

(G31) M. Gurevitch and J. G. Teasdale, Phys. Rev., **76**, 151 (1949). (Fe–S)

(G32) P. Güttinger, Z. Physik, **73**, 169 (1931).

(G33) Gunther-Mohr, Geschwind, and Townes, Phys. Rev., **81**, 289 (1951).

(G34) H. S. Gutowsky and R. E. McClure, Phys. Rev., **81**, 276 (1951).

(H1)   E. Hahn, Phys. Rev., **76,** 461 (1949); **77,** 297 (1950).
(H2)   E. Hahn, Phys. Rev., **80,** 580 (1950).
(H3)   O. Halpern and T. Holstein, Phys. Rev., **59,** 560 (1941).
(H4)   O. Halpern, Phys. Rev., **72,** 245 (1947).
(H5)   D. R. Hamilton, Phys. Rev., **56,** 30 (1939).   (In–Z)
(H6)   D. R. Hamilton, Am. J. Phys., **9,** 319 (1941).
(H7)   M. Hammermesh, Phys. Rev., **73,** 638 (1948).
(H7a)   M. Hammermesh, Phys. Rev., **79,** 888 (1950).
(H8)   H. Hansen, Naturwiss., **15,** 163 (1927).   (Ne–S)
(H8a)   O. Haxel, J. H. D. Jensen, and H. E. Suess, Naturwiss., **35,** 376 (1948); **36,** 153 and 155 (1949); Phys. Rev., **75,** 1766 (1949); Zeits. f. Phys., **128,** 295 (1950).
(H9)   T. C. Hardy and S. Millman, Phys. Rev., **61,** 459 (1942).   (In–A)
(H10)   A. Harvey and F. A. Jenkins, Phys. Rev., **35,** 789 (1930).   (Li–B)
(H10a) J. Hatton, B. V. Rollin, and E. F. Seymour, Phys. Rev., **83,** 672 (1951).
(H11)   R. H. Hay, Phys. Rev., **60,** 75 (1941).   (C, Ba–M)
(H12)   K. Hedfeld and R. Mecke, Z. Physik, **64,** 151 (1930); W. H. J. Childs and R. Mecke, Z. Physik, **64,** 162 (1930).   (H, C–B)
(H13)   M. Heyden and H. Kopfermann, Z. Physik, **108,** 232 (1938).   (Sr–S)
(H14)   M. Heyden and R. Ritschl, Z. Physik, **108,** 739 (1938).   (Al–S)
(H15)   Hipple, Sommer, and Thomas, Phys. Rev., **76,** 1877 (1949); **80,** 487 (1950).   (H–R)
(H16)   J. A. Hipple, private communication.   (H)
(H16a) D. Hughes and C. Eckart, Phys. Rev., **36,** 694 (1930).
(H17)   D. Hughes, Wallace, and Holtzman, Phys. Rev., **73,** 1277 (1948).
(H18)   H. Hughes, Phys. Rev., **72,** 614 (1947).
(H19)   D. Hughes and M. T. Burgy, Phys. Rev., **81,** 498 (1951).
(H20)   D. M. Hunten, Phys. Rev., **78,** 806 (1950).   (Sc)
(H21)   E. Hylleraas and P. R. Skavlem, Phys .Rev., **79,** 117 (1950).
(H22)   J. Hatton and B. V. Rollin, Proc. Roy. Soc. (London), **A199,** 222 (1949).
(H23)   D. R. Hamilton, Am. J. Phys., **9,** 319 (1947).
(I1)   D. Inglis, Phys. Rev., **53,** 470 (1938).
(I2)   D. Inglis, Phys. Rev., **55,** 329 (1939).
(I3)   D. Inglis, Phys. Rev., **53,** 880 (1938).
(I4)   D. Inglis, Phys. Rev., **60,** 837 (1941).
(I5)   D. J. E. Ingram, Proc. Phys. Soc. (London), **A162,** 664 (1949).
(J1)   V. Jaccarino and J. G. King, Phys. Rev., **83,** 471 (1951) and **84,** 852 (1951).
(J2)   D. A. Jackson, Z. Physik, **74,** 291 (1932); **75,** 229 (1932).   (Ga–S)
(J3)   D. A. Jackson, Z. Physik, **80,** 59 (1932).   (In–S)
(J4)   D. A. Jackson, Proc. Roy. Soc. (London), **A143,** 455 (1933).   (Cs–S)
(J5)   L. Jackson and H. Kuhn, Proc. Roy. Soc. (London), **A148,** 335 (1935).
(J6)   D. A. Jackson and H. Kuhn, Proc. Roy. Soc. (London), **A158,** 372 (1937); **A164,** 48 (1939).   (Ag, As–S)
(J7)   B. Jaeckel and H. Kopfermann, Z. Physik, **99,** 492 (1936); B. Jaeckel, Z. Physik, **100,** 513 (1936).   (Pt–S)
(J8)   C. D. Jeffries, Phys. Rev., **78,** 83 (1950).
(J9)   C. Jen, Phys. Rev., **72,** 986 (1947).
(J10)   C. Jen, Phys. Rev., **74,** 1396 (1948).
(J11)   C. K. Jen, Phys. Rev., **78,** 339A (1950).   (S–W)
(J12)   C. K. Jen, unpublished work.

(J13)   F. A. Jenkins and M. Ashley, Phys. Rev., **39**, 552A (1932); M. F. Ashley, Phys. Rev., **44**, 919 (1933). (P–B)

(J14)   F. A. Jenkins, Phys. Rev., **72**, 169A (1947); **73**, 639 (1948); **74**, 355 (1948). (C–B)

(J15)   J. Joffe and H. C. Urey, Phys. Rev., **43**, 761 (1933); J. Joffe, Phys. Rev., **45**, 468 (1934). (Na–B)

(J15a) C. M. Johnson, W. Gordy, and R. Livingston, Phys. Rev., **83**, 1249 (1951).

(J16)   E. G. Jones, Proc. Phys. Soc. (London), **45**, 625 (1933).   (Cd–S)

(J17)   E. G. Jones, Nature, **132**, 781 (1933); Proc. Roy. Soc. (London), **A144**, 587 (1934).   (Xe–S)

(K1)   F. Kalckar and E. Teller, Proc. Roy. Soc. (London), **A150**, 520 (1935).

(K2)   H. Kallman and H. Schüler, Ergeb. exakt. Naturwiss., **11**, 134 (1932). (Ba–S)

(K3)   Kanai, Kobayasi, Kokaji, Progr. Theor. Phys., **2**, 151 (1947).

(K4)   R. Karplus and N. M. Kroll, Phys. Rev., **77**, 536 (1950).

(K5)   A. Kastler, J. phys. radium, **11**, 255 (1950) and Physica, **17**, 191 (1951).

(K6)   T. Kawada, Proc. Phys.-Math. Soc. Japan, **20**, 653 (1938).   (Os–S)

(K7)   Kellogg, Rabi, and Zacharias, Phys. Rev., **50**, 472 (1936).

(K8)   Kellogg, Rabi, Ramsey, and Zacharias, Phys. Rev., **55**, 318 (1939); **57**, 677 (1940). (H–M)

(K9)   Kellogg, Rabi, Ramsey, and Zacharias, Phys. Rev., **56**, 728 (1939).   (H–M)

(K10)   J. M. B. Kellogg and S. Millman, Revs. Mod. Phys., **18**, 323 (1946). (Kr–A)

(K11)   Kellogg and Millman, Revs. Mod. Phys., **18**, 323 (1946).

(K12)   Kelly, Schawlow, Gray, and Crawford, Phys. Rev., **77**, 745A (1950) and **80**, 295 (1950).

(K12a) K. G. Kessler and W. F. Meggers, Phys. Rev., **80**, 905 (1950).

(K13)   Kligman, J. Exptl. Theoret. Phys. U.S.S.R., **18**, 346 (1948).

(K14)   W. D. Knight, Phys. Rev., **76**, 1259 (1949).

(K15)   W. D. Knight and V. W. Cohen, Phys. Rev., **76**, 1421 (1949).   (V–R)

(K15a) S. Koenig, A. G. Prodell, and P. Kusch, Phys. Rev., **83**, 687 (1951).

(K16)   J. Koch and E. Rasmussen, Phys. Rev., **76**, 1417 (1949).   (Ne, Kr–S)

(K17)   J. Koch and E. Rasmussen, Phys. Rev., **77**, 722 (1950).   (Xe–S)

(K17a) W. Kohn and N. Bloembergen, Phys. Rev., **80**, 913 (1950).

(K18)   Kolsky, Phipps, Ramsey, and Silsbee, Phys. Rev., **79**, 883 (1950); **80**, 483 (1950); **81**, 1061 (1951) and Phys. Rev., **87**, 395 (1952).

(K19)   H. Kopfermann, Naturwiss., **19**, 400 (1931); Z. Physik, **75**, 363 (1932). (Pb–S)

(K20)   H. Kopfermann, Z. Physik, **73**, 437 (1932).   (Cs–S)

(K21)   H. Kopfermann, Naturwiss., **21**, 24 (1933); Z. Physik, **83**, 417 (1933); H. Kopfermann and H. Krüger, Z. Physik, **103**, 485 (1936).   (Rb–S)

(K22)   H. Kopfermann and N. Wieth-Knudsen, Z. Physik, **85**, 353 (1933).   (Kr–S)

(K23)   H. Kopfermann, Naturwiss., **39**, 704 (1933); H. Kopfermann and E. Rindal, Z. Physik, **87**, 460 (1934).   (Xe–S)

(K24)   H. Kopfermann and E. Rasmussen, Naturwiss., **22**, 291 (1934).   (Co–S)

(K25)   H. Kopfermann and E. Rasmussen, Naturwiss., **22**, 418 (1934); Z. Physik, **98**, 624 (1936).   (V–S)

(K26)   H. Kopfermann and E. Rasmussen, Z. Physik, **92**, 82 (1934).   (Sc–S)

(K27)   H. Kopfermann and H. Wittke, Z. Physik, **105**, 16 (1937).   (Sc–S)

(K28)   H. Kopfermann and H. Krüger, Z. Physik, **105**, 389 (1937).   (Sc–S)

(K29)   H. Kopfermann, *Kernmomente*, Akademisch Verlagsesellschaft, M. B. H. Leipzig, 1940, and Edwards Bros., Ann Arbor, Michigan.

(K30)   H. Kopfermann and D. Meyer, Z. Physik, **124**, 685 (1948).   (W–S)

(K31)   H. Kopfermann and W. Walcher, Z. Physik, **122**, 465 (1944).

(K32)   H. Kopfermann, Z. Physik, **126**, 344 (1949).

(K33)   H. Kopfermann, private communication.   (Be)

(K33a) H. Kopfermann, R. Martin, and W. Walcher, Naturwiss., **38**, 68 (1951).

(K34)   H. Korsching, Z. Physik, **109**, 349 (1938).   (Kr, Xe–S)

(K35)   R. Kronig, Naturwiss., **16**, 335 (1928).   (N–B)

(K36)   H. Krüger, Z. Physik, **111**, 467 (1938).   (N–B)

(K36a) H. Kuhn and H. Woodgate, Proc. Phys. Soc. (London), **A63**, 830 (1950); Nature, **166**, 906 (1951).

(K37)   Kusch, Millman, and Rabi, Phys. Rev., **55**, 666 (1939).   (Be–M)

(K38)   Kusch, Millman, and Rabi, Phys. Rev., **55**, 1176 (1939).   (N, K, Cs–M)

(K39)   P. Kusch and S. Millman, Phys. Rev., **56**, 527 (1939).   (Cl, Rb–M)

(K40)   Kusch, Millman, and Rabi, Phys. Rev., **57**, 765 (1940).   (K–A)

(K41)   H. Schüler and Jones, Z. Physik, **77**, 802 (1932).

(K42)   P. Kusch and H. M. Foley, Phys. Rev., **74**, 250 (1948).   (In–M)

(K43)   P. Kusch, Phys. Rev., **75**, 887 (1949).   (Li–A)

(K44)   P. Kusch and H. Taub, Phys. Rev., **75**, 1477 (1949).   (Li, Na, K, Rb, Cs–M)

(K45)   P. Kusch, Phys. Rev., **76**, 138 (1949).   (Li–A)

(K46)   P. Kusch and A. K. Mann, Phys. Rev., **76**, 707 (1949).   (Li–A)

(K47)   P. Kusch, Phys. Rev., **78**, 615 (1950).   (Ga–M)

(L1)   W. Lamb, Phys. Rev., **60**, 817 (1941).

(L2)   A. Landé, Z. Physik, **25**, 46 (1924).

(L3)   B. Lasarew and L. Schubnikow, Physik. Z. Sowjetunion, **11**, 445 (1937).

(L4)   Lee, Carlson, Fabricand, and Rabi, Phys. Rev., **78**, 340A (1950).

(L5)   E. C. Levinthal, Phys. Rev., **78**, 204 (1950).

(L6)   H. Lew, Phys. Rev., **74**, 1550 (1948).   (Al–A)

(L7)   H. Lew, Phys. Rev., **76**, 1086 (1949).   (Al–A)

(L8)   G. Lindström, Phys. Rev., **78**, 817 (1950); Arkiv Fysik, **4**, 1 (1951).

(L9)   Livingston, Gilliam, and Gordy, Phys. Rev., **76**, 149 (1949).   (I–W)

(L9a)   R. Livingston, Phys. Rev., **82**, 289 (1951).

(L10)   Lopes, Phys. Rev., **78**, 36 (1950).

(L10a) F. Low, Phys. Rev., **77**, 361 (1950).

(L10b) F. Low and E. E. Salpeter, Phys. Rev., **83**, 478 (1951).

(L11)   V. Low and C. H. Townes, Phys. Rev., **75**, 529 (1949).   (O, S–W)

(L12)   J. M. Luttinger, Phys. Rev., **74**, 893 (1948).

(L13)   J. M. Luttinger, Phys. Rev., **75**, 309, 1277 (1949).

(L14)   J. M. Lyshede and E. Rasmussen, Z. Physik, **104**, 434 (1937).   (Zn–S)

(M1)   J. E. Mack and O. H. Arroe, Phys. Rev., **76**, 173 (1949); and unpublished work.   (Se–S)

(M2)   J. E. Mack and O. H. Arroe, Phys. Rev., **76**, 1002 (1949).   (Te–S)

(M3)   J. E. Mack, Revs. Mod. Phys., **22**, 64 (1950).

(M4)   E. Majorana, Nuovo cimento, **9**, 43 (1932).

(M5)   J. H. Manley, Phys. Rev., **49**, 921 (1936).   (K–Z)

(M6)   J. H. Manley and S. Millman, Phys. Rev., **51**, 19 (1937).   (Li–Z)

(M7)   A. K. Mann and P. Kusch, Phys. Rev., **77**, 427 (1950); **77**, 435 (1950).   (In–A)

(M8)   Margenau and Murphy, *Mathematics of Physics and Chemistry*, D. Van Nostrand Co., New York, 1943.

(M9)   H. Margenau, Phys. Rev., **57**, 383 (1940).
(M10)   H. Margenau and E. Wigner, Phys. Rev., **58**, 103 (1940).
(M11)   M. Mayer, Phys. Rev., **74**, 235 (1948); **78**, 16, 22 (1950).
(M12)   W. W. Meeks and R. A. Fisher, Phys. Rev., **72**, 451 (1947).   (Nb–S)
(M12a) C. L. McGinnis, Phys. Rev., **81**, 734 (1951).   (Ag, Cd, In, Sn–D)
(M13)   Meggers, King, and Bacher, Phys. Rev., **38**, 1258 (1931).   (Re–S)
(M14)   K. W. Meissner and K. Luft, Ann. Physik, **28**, 667 (1937).
(M14a) C. Millar, G. Bartholomew, and B. Kinsey, Phys. Rev., **81**, 150 (1951).
(M14b) S. L. Miller, A. Javan, and C. H. Townes, Phys. Rev., **82**, 454 (1951).
(M15)   S. Millman, Phys. Rev., **47**, 739 (1935).   (K–A)
(M16)   S. Millman and M. Fox, Phys. Rev., **50**, 220 (1936).   (Rb–Z)
(M17)   Millman, Rabi, and Zacharias, Phys. Rev., **53**, 384 (1938).   (In–Z)
(M18)   S. Millman, Phys. Rev., **55**, 628 (1939).
(M19)   Millman, Kusch, and Rabi, Phys. Rev., **56**, 165 (1939).   (B–M)
(M20)   S. Millman and P. Kusch, Phys. Rev., **56**, 303 (1939).   (Al–M)
(M21)   S. Millman and P. Kusch, Phys. Rev., **58**, 438 (1940).
(M22)   S. Millman and P. Kusch, Phys. Rev., **60**, 91 (1941).   (H, Li, F, Na–M)
(M23)   R. Minkowski, Z. Physik, **95**, 284 (1935).
(M23a) H. Miyazawa, Progr. Theor. Phys., **6**, 263 (1951).
(M24)   K. R. More, Phys. Rev., **46**, 470 (1934); **47**, 256A (1935).   (Co–S)
(M25)   N. F. Mott, Proc. Roy. Soc. (London), **A126**, 259 (1930).
(M26)   S. Mrozowski, Phys. Rev., **57**, 207 (1940).   (Hg–S)
(M27)   R. S. Mulliken, Trans. Faraday Soc., **25**, 634 (1929).   (He, C, O–B)
(M28)   K. Murakawa, Z. Physik, **72**, 793 (1931).   (Mg, Zn, Sn, Pb–S)
(M29)   K. Murakawa, Sci. Papers Inst. Phys. Chem. Research Tokyo, **18**, 304 (1932).   (Kr, Ba–S)
(M30)   K. Murakawa, Sci. Papers Inst. Phys. Chem. Research Tokyo, **20**, 285 (1933); Z. Physik, **109**, 162 (1938).   (I–S)
(M31)   K. Murakawa, Z. Physik, **114**, 651 (1939).   (I–S)
(M32)   K. Murakawa and S. Suwa, Phys. Rev., **76**, 433 (1949).   (Sb–S)
(M33)   K. Murakawa, unpublished work, and Phys. Rev., **82**, 967 (1951).   (As, Ir–S)
(M34)   G. M. Murphy and H. Johnston, Phys. Rev., **46**, 95 (1934).   (H–B)
(N1)   Nafe, Nelson, and Rabi, Phys. Rev., **71**, 914 (1947).
(N2)   J. Nafe and E. Nelson, Phys. Rev., **73**, 718 (1948); **75**, 1194 (1949).
(N3)   Nagle, Julian, and Zacharias, Phys. Rev., **72**, 971 (1947).
(N4)   D. E. Nagle, Phys. Rev., **76**, 847 (1949).   (Cs–A)
(N5)   S. M. Naudé and A. Christy, Phys. Rev., **37**, 490 (1931).   (S–B)
(N6)   G. F. Newell, Phys. Rev., **77**, 141 (1950).   (H–calc)
(N7)   G. F. Newell, Phys. Rev., **78**, 711 (1950).
(N7a)   G. F. Newell, Phys. Rev., **80**, 476 (1950).
(N8)   W. A. Nierenberg and N. F. Ramsey, Phys. Rev., **72**, 1075 (1947).
(N9)   W. A. Nierenberg, I. J. Rabi, and M. Slotnick, Phys. Rev., **73**, 1430 (1948).
(N10)   L. Nordheim, Phys. Rev., **75**, 1894 (1949).
(N11)   A. Nordsieck, Phys. Rev., **58**, 310 (1940).
(O1)   S. A. Ochs, R. A. Logan, and P. Kusch, Phys. Rev., **78**, 184 (1950).
(O2)   E. Olsson, Z. Physik, **90**, 138 (1934).   (Se–B)
(O3)   E. Olsson, Z. Physik, **100**, 656 (1936).   (S–B)
(O4)   L. S. Ornstein and W. R. van Wijk, Z. Physik, **49**, 315 (1928); W. R. van Wijk, Z. Physik, **59**, 313 (1930).   (N–B)

(O5)   Bene, Denis and Extermoun, Phys. Rev., **78**, 66 (1950). (Ga)
(P1)   G. Pake, J. Chem. Phys., **16**, 327 (1948); Am. J. Phys., **18**, 438, 473 (1950).
(P2)   F. Paschen and J. S. Campbell, Naturwiss., **22**, 136 (1934). (In–S)
(P3)   W. Paul, Z. Physik, **117**, 774 (1941). (Be–S)
(P4)   W. Pauli, Naturwiss., **12**, 741 (1924).
(P5)   W. Pauli, *Handbuch der Physik*, Vol. 24, Part 1, Julius Springer, Berlin, and Edwards Bros., Ann Arbor, Michigan.
(P6)   W. Pauli, Phys. Rev., **58**, 716 (1940).
(P7)   W. Pauli and S. Dancoff, Phys. Rev., **62**, 85 (1942).
(P8)   B. O. Peirce, *A Short Table of Integrals*, Ginn & Co., Boston, 1899.
(P9)   R. P. Penrose, Nature, **163**, 992 (1949).
(P10)   H. Poss, *Nuclear Moment Table*, Brookhaven National Laboratory, Upton, New York (Brookhaven Report BNL 1-5, 1949).
(P11)   H. L. Poss, Phys. Rev., **75**, 600 (1949). (C, F, Tl–R)
(P12)   R. V. Pound, Phys. Rev., **72**, 1273 (1947). (Br–R)
(P13)   R. V. Pound, Phys. Rev., **73**, 523 (1948). (Cu–R)
(P14)   R. V. Pound, Phys. Rev., **73**, 1112; erratum, **74**, 228 (1948). (P, Ga, I–R)
(P15)   R. V. Pound, Phys. Rev., **79**, 685 (1950); Phys. Rev., **76**, 1410 (1949).
(P16)   R. V. Pound, Phys. Rev., **81**, 156 (1951).
(P16a) P. Preiswerk, Helv. Phys. Acta, **23**, 7 (1950).
(P17)   R. D. Present and E. Feenberg, Phys. Rev., **78**, 328A (1950).
(P18)   H. Primakoff, Phys. Rev., **72**, 118 (1947).
(P19)   W. G. Proctor, Phys. Rev., **75**, 522 (1949). (Tl–R)
(P20)   W. G. Proctor, Phys. Rev., **76**, 684 (1949). (Sn, Pb–R)
(P21)   W. G. Proctor and F. C. Yu, Phys. Rev., **76**, 1728 (1949). (Cd, Sn, Pt, Hg–R)
(P22)   W. G. Proctor and F. C. Yu, unpublished work, and Phys. Rev., **81**, 20 (1951). (N, Cl, V, Mn, Co, Cd, Sn, Pt, Hg, Pb–R)
(P23)   W. G. Proctor and F. C. Yu, Phys. Rev., **77**, 716 (1950). (Mn, Co, Cl–R)
(P24)   W. G. Proctor and F. C. Yu, Phys. Rev., **77**, 717 (1950).
(P25)   W. G. Proctor and F. C. Yu, Phys. Rev., **78**, 471 (1950). (Xe, Bi, Sc, Sb–R)
(P26)   W. G. Proctor, Phys. Rev., **79**, 35 (1950). (Tl, Sn, Cd, Pb–R)
(P26a) A. G. Prodell and P. Kusch, Phys. Rev., **79**, 1009 (1950).
(P27)   Purcell, Torrey, and Pound, Phys. Rev., **69**, 37 (1946).
(P28)   E. M. Purcell and N. F. Ramsey, Phys. Rev., **78**, 807 (1950).
(P29)   E. M. Purcell, private communication.
(P30)   E. M. Purcell and R. V. Pound, Phys. Rev., **81**, 279 (1951).
(R1)   I. I. Rabi and V. W. Cohen, Phys. Rev., **46**, 707 (1934). (Na–Z)
(R2)   Rabi, Kellogg, and Zacharias, Phys. Rev., **46**, 157 (1934).
(R3)   Rabi, Kellogg, and Zacharias, Phys. Rev., **46**, 163 (1934).
(R4)   I. Rabi, Phys. Rev., **49**, 324 (1936).
(R5)   I. Rabi, Phys. Rev., **51**, 652 (1937).
(R6)   Rabi, Millman, Kusch, and Zacharias, Phys. Rev., **55**, 526 (1939).
(R7)   G. Racah, Z. Physik, **76**, 431 (1931).
(R8)   G. Racah, Nature, **129**, 723 (1932).
(R9)   S. Rafalowski, Acta Phys. Polon., **2**, 119 (1933). (Se, Te–S)
(R9a)   J. Rainwater, Phys. Rev., **79**, 432 (1950).
(R10)   N. Ramsey, Phys. Rev., **58**, 226 (1940).
(R11)   N. F. Ramsey, Phys. Rev., **74**, 286 (1948).
(R12)   N. F. Ramsey, Phys. Rev., **77**, 567 (1950).

(R12a) N. F. Ramsey, Phys. Rev., **78**, 221 (1950).

(R13)   N. F. Ramsey, Phys. Rev., **78**, 695 (1950).

(R14)   N. F. Ramsey, Phys. Rev., **78**, 699 (1950).

(R14a) N. F. Ramsey, Phys. Rev., **79**, 1010 (1950).

(R15)   N. F. Ramsey and R. V. Pound, Phys. Rev., **81**, 278 (1951).

(R15a) N. F. Ramsey, Physica, **17**, 303 (1951).

(R15b) N. F. Ramsey, Physica, **17**, 388 (1951).

(R16)   N. F. Ramsey, Phys. Rev., **83**, 540 (1951).

(R16a) N. F. Ramsey and H. B. Silsbee, Phys. Rev., **84**, 506 (1951).

(R16b) N. F. Ramsey and E. M. Purcell, Phys. Rev., **85**, 143 (1952).

(R16c) N. F. Ramsey, Physica, **17**, 303 (1951).

(R17)   N. F. Ramsey, Phys. Rev., **85**, 60 (1952).

(R17a) N. F. Ramsey, Phys. Rev., **87**, 1075 (1952); **89**, 527 (1953).

(R17b) N. F. Ramsey, Phys. Rev., **86**, 243 (1952).

(R17c) N. F. Ramsey and U. Liddel, J. Chem. Phys., **19**, 1608 (1952).

(R18)   A. S. Rao, Z. Physik, **84**, 236 (1933). (As–S)

(R19)   W. Rarita and J. Schwinger, Phys. Rev., **59**, 436 (1941).

(R20)   F. Rasetti, *Proc. Natl. Acad. Sci. U.S.*, **15**, 515 (1929); Nature, **123**, 757 (1929); **124**, 792 (1929). (N–C)

(R21)   E. Rasmussen, Naturwiss., **23**, 69 (1935). (Hf–S)

(R22)   E. Rasmussen, Z. Physik, **102**, 229 (1936). (Co–S)

(R23)   E. Rasmussen, unpublished work. (Xe–S)

(R24)   N. Renzetti, Phys. Rev., **57**, 753 (1940).

(R25)   R. Ritschl, Z. Physik, **79**, 1 (1932). (Cu–S)

(R26)   R. Ritschl and H. Schober, Physik. Z. **38**, 6 (1937). (Ne–S)

(R27)   Roberts, Beers, and Hill, Phys. Rev., **70**, 112 (1946).

(R28)   A. Roberts, Phys. Rev., **72**, 979 (1947). (H–R)

(R29)   A. Roberts, Phys. Rev., **73**, 1405 (1948). (C–W)

(R30)   A. Roberts, unpublished work. (S–W)

(R31)   E. H. Rogers and H. H. Staub, Phys. Rev., **76**, 980 (1949). (n, H–R)

(R32)   M. E. Rose and H. A. Bethe, Phys. Rev., **51**, 205 (1937).

(R32a) M. E. Rose, Phys. Rev., **75**, 213 (1949).

(R33)   L. Rosenfeld, *Theory of Nuclear Forces*, North Holland Publishing Co., Amsterdam, Holland, and Interscience Publishers, Inc., New York, 1949.

(R34)   J. S. Ross, Phys. Rev., **83**, 229 (1951), and unpublished work. (Te, Fe–S)

(R35)   B. V. Rollin, Rep. Phys. Soc., Prog. Phys., **12**, 22 (1948–1949).

(S1)   R. Sachs, Phys. Rev., **69**, 611 (1946).

(S2)   R. Sachs and J. Schwinger, Phys. Rev., **70**, 41 (1946).

(S3)   R. Sachs, Phys. Rev., **72**, 91 (1947).

(S4)   R. Sachs, Phys. Rev., **72**, 312 (1947).

(S5)   Schawlow, Hume, and Crawford, Phys. Rev., **76**, 1876 (1949). (Pb–S)

(S6)   A. L. Schawlow and C. H. Townes, private communication, and Phys. Rev., **82**, 268 (1951). (Se–W)

(S7)   T. Schmidt, Z. Physik, **101**, 486 (1936). (Pt–S)

(S8)   T. Schmidt, Z. Physik, **106**, 358 (1937).

(S9)   T. Schmidt, Z. Physik, **108**, 408 (1938). (Re–S)

(S10)   T. Schmidt, Z. Physik, **112**, 199 (1930). (I–S)

(S11)   T. Schmidt, Naturwiss., **28**, 565 (1940). (Cs–S)

(S12)   T. Schmidt, Z. Physik, **121**, 63 (1943). (Ta–S)

(S13)   H. Schüler and H. Bruck, Z. Physik, **56**, 291 (1929). (Cd, Tl–S)

(S14)   H. Schüler and J. E. Keyston, Z. Physik, **70**, 1 (1931). (Tl–S)

(S15)   H. Schüler and J. E. Keyston, Z. Physik, **72**, 423 (1931). (Hg–S)

(S16)   H. Schüler and Jones, Z. Physik, **77**, 802 (1932).

(S17)   H. Schüler and H. Westmeyer, Naturwiss., **21**, 660 (1933). (Sn–S)

(S18)   H. Schüler and H. Gollnow, Naturwiss., **22**, 511 (1934). (Pa–S)

(S19)   H. Schüler and T. Schmidt, Naturwiss., **22**, 714 (1934). (Lu–S)

(S20)   H. Schüler and H. Gollnow, Naturwiss., **22**, 730 (1934). (Tb–S)

(S21)   H. Schüler and T. Schmidt, Naturwiss., **22**, 758 (1934). (Sc–S)

(S22)   H. Schüler and T. Schmidt, Naturwiss., **22**, 838 (1934). (Y, Rh, Tb, Tm–S)

(S23)   H. Schüler and T. Schmidt, Naturwiss., **23**, 69 (1935). (He–S)

(S24)   H. Schüler and T. Schmidt, Z. Physik, **94**, 457 (1935); **98**, 430 (1935).
        (Cu, As, In, Sb, Eu, Lu, Hg–S)

(S25)   H. Schüler and T. Schmidt, Z. Physik, **95**, 265 (1935). (Lu–S)

(S26)   H. Schüler and T. Schmidt, Z. Physik, **98**, 239 (1935). (Hg–S)

(S27)   H. Schüler and T. Schmidt, Z. Physik, **99**, 717 (1936). (Bi–S)

(S28)   H. Schüler and T. Schmidt, Z. Physik, **100**, 113 (1936). (Cu–S)

(S29)   H. Schüler and M. Marketu, Z. Physik, **102**, 703 (1936). (As–S)

(S30)   H. Schüler and H. Korsching, Z. Physik, **103**, 434 (1936). (Ga–S)

(S31)   H. Schüler and T. Schmidt, Z. Physik, **104**, 468 (1937). (Tn, Tl–S)

(S32)   H. Schüler and H. Korsching, Z. Physik, **105**, 168 (1937). (Cu, Re, Tl–S)

(S33)   Schüler, Roig, and Korsching, Z. Physik, **111**, 165 (1938); H. Schüler and
        H. Korsching, Z. Physik, **111**, 386 (1938). (Xe, Yb–S)

(S34)   H. Schüler and H. Gollnow, Z. Physik, **113**, 1 (1939). (Lu–S)

(S34a) N. A. Schuster and G. E. Pake, Phys. Rev., **81**, 157 (1951).

(S35)   J. Schwinger, Phys. Rev., **51**, 545 (1937).

(S36)   J. Schwinger, Phys. Rev., **52**, 1250 (1937).

(S37)   J. Schwinger, Phys. Rev., **73**, 416 (1948); **76**, 790 (1949).

(S38)   Sheriff, Chambers, and Williams, Phys. Rev., **78**, 476, 482 (1950).
        (Nb, Pr–R)

(S39)   R. E. Sheriff and D. Williams, Phys. Rev., **79**, 175 (1950); **82**, 651 (1951).
        (Sc–R)

(S39a) J. Sheridan and W. Gordy, Phys. Rev., **79**, 513 (1950).

(S40)   L. Sibaiya, Proc. Indian Acad. Sci., **6A**, 229 (1937). (Rh–S)

(S41)   K. Siegbahn and G. Lindström, Nature, **163**, 211 (1949); Arkiv Fysik, **1**,
        193 (1949). (H, Li, F–R)

(S41a) F. E. Simon, Congrès sur le Magnétisme, Strasbourg, **3**, 1 (1939).

(S42)   J. W. Simmons and W. Gordy, Phys. Rev., **73**, 713 (1948).

(S43)   Slotnick and W. Heitler, Phys. Rev., **75**, 1645 (1949).

(S44)   B. Smaller, E. Yasaitis, and H. L. Anderson, Phys. Rev., **80**, 137 (1950);
        83, 813 (1951). (H–R)

(S45)   Smith, Ramsey, and Purcell, private communication.

(S45a) Smith, Tidwell, and Williams, Phys. Rev., **79**, 1007 (1950).

(S45b) K. T. Smith, Nature, **167**, 942 (1951).

(S45c) R. M. Steffen, Phys. Rev., **83**, 166 (1951). (In–D)

(S46)   R. Sternheimer, Phys. Rev., **80**, 102 (1950); **84**, 244 (1951).

(S47)   Strandberg, Wentink, and Hill, Phys. Rev., **75**, 827 (1949). (Se–W)

(S47a) G. L. Stuckenbroeker and J. R. McNally, J. Opt. Soc. Am., **40**, 336
        (1950).

(S47b) S. Suwa, Phys. Rev., **83**, 1258 (1951).

(T1)   H. Taub and P. Kusch, Phys. Rev., **75**, 1481 (1949). (H–M)

(T2)   J. B. Taylor, Z. Physik, **57**, 242 (1929).

(T3)   A. Thellung and F. Villars, Phys. Rev., **73**, 924 (1948).

(T4)   Thomas, Driscoll, and Hipple, Phys. Rev., **75**, 902, 992 (1949); **78**, 787 (1950). (H–R)

(T5)   H. A. Thomas, Phys. Rev., **80**, 901 (1950).

(T6)   S. Tolansky, Proc. Roy. Soc. (London), **A130**, 558 (1931). (Hg–S)

(T7)   S. Tolansky, Proc. Roy. Soc. (London), **A136**, 585 (1932). (Br–S)

(T8)   S. Tolansky, Nature, **129**, 652 (1932); Proc. Roy. Soc. (London), **A137**, 541 (1932). (As–S)

(T9)   S. Tolansky, Nature, **132**, 318 (1933); Proc. Roy. Soc. (London), **A144**, 574 (1934). (Sn–S)

(T10)   S. Tolansky, Proc. Roy. Soc. (London), **A144**, 574 (1934). (S)

(T11)   S. Tolansky, *Fine Structure in Line Spectra and Nuclear Spin* and *High Resolution Spectroscopy*. Methuen and Co., Ltd., London, 1948.

(T12)   S. Tolansky and E. Lee, Proc. Roy. Soc. (London), **A158**, 110 (1937).

(T13)   S. Tolansky, Proc. Roy. Soc. (London), **A170**, 205 (1939).

(T14)   S. Tolansky and S. A. Trivedi, Proc. Roy. Soc. (London), **A175**, 366 (1940). (Br–S)

(T15)   S. Tolansky and G. O. Forester, Phil. Mag., **32**, 315 (1941). (Sn–S)

(T16)   S. Tolansky, British AEC Report, 1945, and MDDC—333. (U–S)

(T17)   D. H. Tomboulian and R. F. Bacher, Phys. Rev., **58**, 52 (1940). (Sb–S)

(T18)   F. S. Tomkins, Phys. Rev., **73**, 1214 (1948); **84**, 168 (1951). (Np–S)

(T19)   H. Torrey, Phys. Rev., **59**, 293 (1941).

(T20)   H. Torrey, Phys. Rev., **75**, 1326 (1949); **76**, 1059 (1949).

(T21)   C. H. Townes and W. R. Smythe, Phys. Rev., **56**, 1210 (1939). (C–B)

(T22)   C. H. Townes, Phys. Rev., **71**, 909 (1947).

(T23)   Townes, Holden, Bardeen, and Merritt, Phys. Rev., **71**, 644 (1947). (N, Cl, Br–W)

(T24)   Townes, Holden, and Merritt, Phys. Rev., **72**, 513 (1947). (C, S–W)

(T25)   C. H. Townes and S. Geschwind, Phys. Rev., **74**, 626 (1948); Townes, Holden, and Merritt, Phys. Rev., **74**, 1113 (1948); C. H. Townes and B. P. Dailey, J. Chem. Phys., **17**, 782 (1949). (N, O, S, Cl, Br, I–W)

(T26)   C. H. Townes and L. C. Aamodt, Phys. Rev., **76**, 691 (1949). (Cl–W)

(T27)   Townes, Mays, and Dailey, Phys. Rev., **76**, 700 (1949); **81**, 940 (1951). (Si, Ge–W)

(T28)   Townes, Foley, and Low, Phys. Rev., **76**, 1415 (1949).

(T29)   C. H. Townes, C. Herring, and W. D. Knight, Phys. Rev., **77**, 851 (1950).

(T30)   C. H. Townes, S. Geschwind, and H. Minden, Phys. Rev., **78**, 174 (1950).

(T30a) B. Touschek, Phil. Mag., **42**, 312 (1951).

(T31)   J. Trischka, Phys. Rev., **74**, 718 (1948).

(V1)   J. Van Vleck, *Electric and Magnetic Susceptibilities*, Oxford University Press, Clarendon, 1932.

(V2)   J. Van Vleck, Phys. Rev., **71**, 468 (1947).

(V3)   J. Van Vleck, Phys. Rev., **74**, 1168 (1948).

(V4)   B. Venkatesachar and L. Sibaiya, Proc. Indian Acad. Sci., **2a**, 203 (1935); L. Sibaiya, Phys. Rev., **56**, 768 (1930). (Ir–S)

(W1)   R. G. Watts and Williams, Phys. Rev., **72**, 263 (1947).

(W2)   F. Villars, Phys. Rev., **72**, 256 (1948).

(W2a)   H. Walchli, R. Livingston, and G. Herbert, Phys. Rev., **82**, 97 (1951).

(W3)   R. K. Wangsness, Phys. Rev., **78**, 620 (1950).

(W4)   Weiss, Strandberg, Lawrance, and Loomis, Phys. Rev., **78**, 202 (1950). (B–W)

(W5)   H. E. White, Phys. Rev., **34**, 1397 (1929); Gibbs, White, and Tuedy, Proc. Natl. Acad. Sci. U.S., **15**, 642 (1929). (Pr–S)

(W6)   H. E. White and R. Ritschl, Phys. Rev., **35**, 208 (1930); erratum, **36**, 1146 (1930); H. E. White and R. Ritschl, Phys. Rev., **36**, 1146 (1930). (Mn–S)

(W7)   H. E. White and O. E. Anderson, Phys. Rev., **44**, 128A (1933). (La–S)

(W8)   H. E. White, *Introduction to Atomic Spectra*, McGraw-Hill Book Co., New York, 1934, pp. 130, 361.

(W9)   G. C. Wick, Phys. Rev., **73**, 51 (1948).

(W10)   E. Wigner, *Gruppentheorie und ihre Anwendurg auf die Quantenmechanik der Atomspektren*, Friedr. Vieweg and Sohn Akt.-Ges., Graunschweig, Germany, 1931, and Edwards Bros., Ann Arbor, Michigan, 1944.

(W11)   T. F. Wimett, M.I.T. Research Laboratory of Electronics Report, July 1949, p. 29. (H–R)

(W12)   H. Wittke, Z. Physik, **116**, 547 (1940). (Y, La, Bi–S)

(W13)   R. W. Wood and G. H. Dieke, J. Chem. Phys., **6**, 908 (1938); **8**, 351 (1940). (N–B)

(W14)   H.Weyl, *The Classical Groups*, Princeton University Press, Princeton, 1939, pp. 149ff.

(X1)   Authorities who do not want to be quoted.

(Y1)   E. Yasaitis and B. Smaller, Phys. Rev., **82**, 750 (1951).

(Z1)   J. R. Zacharias and J. M. B. Kellogg, Phys. Rev., **57**, 570A (1940). (N–M)

(Z2)   J. R. Zacharias, Phys. Rev., **61**, 270 (1942). (K–A)

(Z3)   Zeeman, Gisolf, and de Bruin, Nature, **128**, 637 (1931). (Re–S)

(Z4)   Zeiger, Bolef, and Rabi, Phys. Rev., **78**, 340A (1950).

(Z5)   J. R. Zimmerman and D. Williams, Phys. Rev., **76**, 350 (1949). (H, Li, B, F, Na, Al, Cu, Br, Rb, I–R)

(Z6)   Data added in proof and taken from the tables of P. F. A. Klinkenberg, Revs. Mod. Phys., **24**, 63 (1952). References to the original articles are given by Klinkenberg.

(Z7)   Wang, Townes, Schawlow, and Holden, Phys. Rev., **86**, 809 (1952).

(ZA1)   A. Abragam and M. H. L. Pryce, Proc. Roy. Soc. (London), **A205**, 136 (1951).

(ZA2)   N. L. Alpert, Phys. Rev., **75**, 398 (1949).

(ZA2a) P. W. Anderson, Phys. Rev., **80**, 511 (1950).

(ZA3)   E. R. Andrew and R. Bersohn, J. Chem. Phys., **18**, 159 (1950).

(ZA4)   E. R. Andrew, J. Chem. Phys., **18**, 607 (1950).

(ZA5)   Arnold, Dharmatti, and Packard, J. Chem. Phys., **19**, 507 (1951).

(ZA6)   P. Axel, Phys. Rev., **80**, 104 (1950).

(ZB1)   D. M. S. Bagguley and J. H. E. Griffiths, Proc. Roy. Soc. (London), **A201**, 366 (1950).

(ZB2)   W. Barkas, Phys. Rev., **55**, 691 (1939).

(ZB3)   Barnes, Bray, and Ramsey, Phys. Rev. (1954).

(ZB4)   H. Bayer, Z. Physik, **130**, 227 (1951).

(ZB5)   R. Beringer, Phys. Rev., **70**, 53 (1946).

(ZB6)   Beringer, Castle, and Rawson, Phys. Rev., **78**, 581 (1950); **80**, 114 (1950); **81**, 82 (1951); **86**, 607 (1952).

(ZB7)   A. Berthelot, J. phys. et radium, **3**, 17, 52 (1942).

(ZB8)   B. Bleaney and R. P. Penrose, Nature, **157**, 339 (1946); Proc. Roy. Soc. (London), **A189**, 358 (1947).

(ZB9)   B. Bleaney and R. P. Penrose, Phys. Rev., **70**, 775 (1946); Proc. Phys. Soc. (London), **60**, 83 (1948).

(ZB10)   B. Bleaney and R. P. Penrose, Proc. Phys. Soc. (London), **60**, 395 (1948).

(ZB11)   B. Bleaney, Physica, **17**, 169 (1951).

(ZB12)   N. Bloembergen, Ph.D. Thesis, Leiden (1948); Physica, **15**, 380, 588 (1949).

(ZB13)   N. Bloembergen, Phys. Rev., **78**, 572 (1950).

(ZB14)   N. Bloembergen and W. C. Dickinson, Phys. Rev., **79**, 179 (1950).

(ZB15)   N. Bloembergen, Physica, **16**, 950 (1950).

(ZB16)   Burkhalter, Anderson, Smith, and Gordy, Phys. Rev., **79**, 651 (1950).

(ZC1)   H. Y. Carr and E. M. Purcell, Phys. Rev., **88**, 415 (1952).

(ZC2)   P. Chanson, Acad. Sci. (Paris), **226**, 997 (1948).

(ZC3)   C. E. Cleeton and N. H. Williams, Phys. Rev., **45**, 234 (1934).

(ZC4)   Cummerow, Halliday, and Moore, Phys. Rev., **72**, 1233 (1947).

(ZD1)   Dakin, Good, and Coles, Phys. Rev., **70**, 560 (1946).

(ZD2)   Dailey, Golden, and Wilson, Jr., Phys. Rev., **72**, 871 (1947).

(ZD3)   C. Dean and R. V. Pound, J. Chem. Phys., **20**, 195 (1952).

(ZD4)   P. Debye, *Polar Molecules*, Dover Publications, New York, 1945.

(ZD5)   D. H. Dennison and J. D. Hardy, Phys. Rev., **39**, 938 (1932).

(ZD6)   S. Drell, private communication.

(ZE1)   R. J. Elliott and K. W. H. Stevens, Proc. Phys. Soc. (London), **A63**, 1369 (1951).

(ZE1a)   W. Elsasser, J. phys. et radium, **5**, 625 (1934).

(ZE2)   J. R. Eshbach and M. W. P. Strandberg, Phys. Rev., **85**, 24 (1952).

(ZF1)   Fabricand, Carlson, Lee, and Rabi, Phys. Rev., **86**, 607 (1952).

(ZF2)   E. Feenberg and E. Wigner, Repts. Prog. Phys., **8**, 274 (1942).

(ZF3)   Feenberg, Hammack, and Nordheim, Phys. Rev., **75**, 1968 (1949).

(ZF4)   E. Feenberg, Phys. Rev., **77**, 771 (1950).

(ZF5)   B. T. Feld and W. E. Lamb, Phys. Rev., **67**, 15 (1945).

(ZF6)   B. T. Feld, Ann. Rev. Nuclear Sci. (1952).

(ZF7)   H. M. Foley, Phys. Rev., **69**, 616, 628 (1946).

(ZG1)   R. Gaus and R. G. Loyarte, Ann. Physik, **64**, 209 (1921).

(ZG2)   H. Gaus, Z. Naturforsch., **49**, 721 (1949).

(ZG3)   Gilbert, Roberts, and Griswold, Phys. Rev., **76**, 1723 (1949).

(ZG4)   S. Golden and E. B. Wilson, J. Chem. Phys., **16**, 669 (1948).

(ZG5)   M. Goldhaber and A. Sunyar, Phys. Rev., **83**, 906 (1951).

(ZG6)   M. Goldhaber and R. D. Hill, Revs. Mod. Phys., **24**, 179 (1952).

(ZG7)   C. J. Gorter and J. H. Van Vleck, Phys. Rev., **72**, 1128 (1946).

(ZG8)   J. H. E. Griffiths, Nature, **158**, 670 (1946); Physica, **17**, 253 (1951).

(ZG9)   Griswold, Kip, and Kittel, Phys. Rev., **88**, 951 (1952), private communication.

(ZG10)   H. S. Gutowsky and G. E. Pake, J. Chem. Phys., **16**, 1164 (1948); **18**, 162 (1950).

(ZG11)   Gutowsky, G. B. Kistiakowsky, G. E. Pake, and E. M. Purcell, J. Chem. Phys., **17**, 972 (1949); **18**, 162 (1950).

(ZG12)   Gutowsky, McCall, Slichter, and McNeil, Phys. Rev., **82**, 748 (1951); **84**, 589, 1246 (1951).

(ZG13)   H. S. Gutowsky and A. Saika, J. Chem. Phys. (1953), and private communication.

(ZG14) Proceedings of International Conference on Spectroscopy at Radiofrequencies, Physica, **17**, 169–484 (1951).
(ZH1) E. L. Hahn and D. E. Maxwell, Phys. Rev., **84**, 1246 (1951); **88**, 1070 (1952).
(ZH2) N. J. Harrick and N. F. Ramsey, Phys. Rev., **88**, 228 (1952).
(ZH3) Harrick, Barnes, Bray, and Ramsey, Phys. Rev., **90**, 260 (1953).
(ZH4) J. Hatton and B. V. Rollin, Proc. Roy. Soc. (London), **A199**, 222 (1949).
(ZH5) G. G. Havens, Phys. Rev., **43**, 992 (1933).
(ZH6) W. Heitler and E. Teller, Proc. Roy. Soc. (London), **A155**, 629 (1936).
(ZH7) R. S. Henderson and J. H. Van Vleck, Phys. Rev., **74**, 106 (1948).
(ZH8) R. S. Henderson, Phys. Rev., **74**, 107, 626 (1948).
(ZH9) W. D. Hershberger and J. Turkevitch, Phys. Rev., **71**, 554 (1947).
(ZH10) G. Herzberg, *Spectra of Diatomic Molecules*, D. Van Nostrand Co., New York, 1950.
(ZH11) G. Herzberg, *Infra Red and Ramon Spectra of Polyatomic Molecules*, D. Van Nostrand Co., New York, 1945.
(ZH12) R. D. Hill, Phys. Rev., **76**, 998 (1949); **79**, 1021 (1950).
(ZH12a) R. M. Hill and W. V. Smith, Phys. Rev., **82**, 451 (1951).
(ZH12b) R. R. Howard and W. V. Smith, Phys. Rev., **79**, 128, 132 (1950).
(ZH12c) T. Holstein, Phys. Rev., **79**, 744 (1950).
(ZH13) R. H. Hughes and E. B. Wilson, Phys. Rev., **71**, 562 (1947).
(ZH14) D. Hughes and D. Sherman, Phys. Rev., **78**, 632 (1950).
(ZH15) V. Hughes and L. Grabner, Phys. Rev., **79**, 314 (1950).
(ZH16) C. A. Hutchinson, Phys. Rev., **75**, 1769 (1949).
(ZJ1) H. M. James and A. S. Coolidge, Astrophys. J., **87**, 447 (1938).
(ZJ2) C. K. Jen, Phys. Rev., **74**, 1246 (1948); **76**, 1496 (1949); **81**, 197 (1951).
(ZJ3) Jen, Barghansen, and Stanley, Phys. Rev., **85**, 717A (1952).
(ZJ4) J. Jensen and H. Steinwedel, Naturwiss., **33**, 249 (1946).
(ZJ5) Jensen, Suess, and Haxel, Naturwiss., **35**, 376 (1948); **36**, 153 (1949); Phys. Rev., **75**, 1766 (1949); Z. Physik, **1z8**, 295 (1950).
(ZK1) R. Karplus and J. Schwinger, Phys. Rev., **73**, 1020, 1120 (1948); **74**, 223 (1948).
(ZK1a) P. Kisliuk and C. H. Townes, Natl. Bur. Standards (U.S.), Circ. 518 (1952).
(ZK2) A. F. Kip and R. D. Arnold, Phys. Rev., **75**, 1556 (1949).
(ZK3) C. Kittel, Phys. Rev., **71**, 270 (1947); **73**, 155 (1948); **76**, 743 (1949).
(ZK4) C. Kittel, Revs. Mod. Phys., **21**, 541 (1949).
(ZK4a) C. Kittel, Phys. Rev., **82**, 565 (1951).
(ZK5) J. S. Koehler and D. M. Dennison, Phys. Rev., **57**, 1006 (1940).
(ZK6) J. Korringa, Physica, **16**, 601 (1950).
(ZL1) W. E. Lamb and R. C. Retherford, Phys. Rev., **79**, 549 (1950); **81**, 222 (1951); **85**, 259 (1952); **86**, 1014 (1952).
(ZL2) F. W. Lancaster and W. Gordy, J. Chem. Phys., **19**, 1181 (1951).
(ZL3) L. Landau and E. Lifschitz, Physik. Z. Sowjetunion, **8**, 153 (1935).
(ZL4) Lee, Carlson, Fabricand, and Rabi, Phys. Rev., **86**, 607 (1952).
(ZL5) R. Livingston, J. Chem. Phys., **19**, 1434 (1951).
(ZL6) H. Lu, Phys. Rev., **74**, 416 (1950).
(ZM0a) H. Margenau and S. Bloom, Phys. Rev., **76**, 121 (1949); **79**, 213 (1950).
(ZM0b) J. Mays, Ann. N. Y. Acad. Sci. (1952).
(ZM1) McNeil, Slichter, and Gutowsky, Phys. Rev., **84**, 589 (1951).
(ZM1a) K. B. McAfee, Phys. Rev., **78**, 340 (1950).

(ZM2)   Miller, Kotani, and Townes, Phys. Rev., **86**, 607 (1952).
(ZN0)   G. Newell and R. H. Dicke, Phys. Rev., **81**, 297 (1951).
(ZN1)   H. H. Nielsen, Phys. Rev., **40**, 445 (1932).
(ZN2)   H. H. Nielsen, Revs. Mod. Phys., **23**, 90 (1951).
(ZN3)   L. Nordheim, Phys. Rev., **75**, 1894 (1949).
(ZP1)   M. E. Packard and J. T. Arnold, Phys. Rev., **83**, 210 (1951); J. Chem. Phys., **19**, 1608 (1951).
(ZP1a) L. Pauling, *Nature of the Chemical Bond*, Cornell University Press, Ithaca, N. Y., 1941.
(ZP2)   G. E. Pake and E. M. Purcell, Phys. Rev., **74**, 1184 (1948).
(ZP3)   G. E. Pake, J. Chem. Phys., **16**, 327 (1948).
(ZP4)   G. E. Pake, Am. J. Phys., **18**, 438, 473 (1950).
(ZP5)   Poulis, van den Handel, Ubbink, Poulis, and Gorter, Phys. Rev., **82**, 552 (1951).
(ZP6)   R. V. Pound, Phys. Rev., **72**, 1273 (1948); **73**, 1112 (1948).
(ZP7)   R. V. Pound, Phys. Rev., **79**, 685 (1950).
(ZP8)   R. V. Pound, Phys. Rev., **81**, 156 (1951).
(ZP9)   R. V. Pound, Prog. Nuclear Phys., **2**, 21 (1952).
(ZP10) M. H. L. Pryce, Nature, **162**, 539 (1948).
(ZP11) E. M. Purcell, Physica, **17**, 282 (1951).
(ZR1)   I. I. Rabi, Phys. Rev., **87**, 379 (1952).
(ZR2)   N. F. Ramsey, Phys. Rev., **87**, 1075 (1952).
(ZR3)   N. F. Ramsey, Phys. Rev., **90**, 232 (1953); **90**, 382 (1953).
(ZR4)   N. F. Ramsey, Phys. Rev., **91**, 303 (1953).
(ZR5)   N. F. Ramsey, Science, **117**, 470 (1953).
(ZR6)   F. Reif, Ph.D. Thesis, Harvard University, 1953.
(ZR7)   F. Reif and E. M. Purcell, Phys. Rev., **91**, 631 (1953).
(ZR8)   S. Roberts and A. von Hippel, J. Appl. Phys., **17**, 610 (1946).
(ZS1)   Sachs, Turner, and Purcell, Phys. Rev., **76**, 465, 466 (1949).
(ZS2)   Sanders, Schawlow, Dousmanis, and Townes, Columbia Radiation Laboratory Report, Dec. 31, 1952.
(ZS3)   L. Schiff, *Quantum Mechanics*, McGraw-Hill Book Co., New York, 1949.
(ZS4)   E. E. Schneider and T. S. England, Physica, **17**, 221 (1951).
(ZS5)   N. A. Schuster and G. E. Pake, Phys. Rev., **81**, 157 (1951).
(ZS6)   J. C. Schwartz and J. W. Trischka, Phys. Rev., **88**, 1085 (1952).
(ZS7)   R. Schwartz, Ph.D. Thesis, Harvard University, 1952.
(ZS8)   J. W. Simmons and W. Gordy, Phys. Rev., **73**, 713 (1948).
(ZS9)   Smaller, Yasaitis, Avery, and Hutchison, Phys. Rev., **88**, 414 (1952).
(ZS10) Stitch, Honig, and Townes, Phys. Rev., **86**, 813 (1952).
(ZT1)   C. H. Townes, Phys. Rev., **70**, 665 (1946).
(ZT2)   Townes, Merritt, and Wright, Phys. Rev., **73**, 1334 (1948).
(ZT3)   C. H. Townes and B. P. Dailey, J. Chem. Phys., **17**, 782 (1949).
(ZT4)   C. H. Townes, Physica, **17**, 364 (1951).
(ZT4a) C. H. Townes and A. L. Schawlow, *Microwave Spectroscopy*, McGraw-Hill Book Co., New York (in preparation), and private communications.
(ZT5)   Trounson, Bleil, Wangsness, and Maxwell, Phys. Rev., **79**, 542 (1950).
(ZT6)   Trans. Faraday Soc., **42**, Suppl. (1946). A general discussion of dielectrics.
(ZU1)   Ubbink, Poulis, and Gorter, Physica, **17**, 215 (1951).
(ZU1a) J. Ubbink, Phys. Rev., **86**, 567 (1952).
(ZV1)   J. H. Van Vleck and V. F. Weisskopf, Revs. Mod. Phys., **17**, 227 (1945).

References   159

References   159

(ZV2)   J. H. Van Vleck, Phys. Rev., **71**, 413 (1947).
(ZV3)   J. H. Van Vleck, Phys. Rev., **73**, 1249 (1948); **74**, 1168, 1211 (1948).
(ZV4)   J. H. Van Vleck, Phys. Rev., **78**, 266 (1950).
(ZV5)   J. H. Van Vleck, Phys. Rev., **78**, 272 (1950).
(ZV6)   J. H. Van Vleck, Physica, **17**, 234 (1951).
(ZV7)   J. H. Van Vleck, Ann. N. Y. Acad. Sci., **55**, 928 (1952).
(ZW1)   I. Waller, Z. Physik, **79**, 370 (1932).
(ZW1a) H. E. Walchli, *Table of Nuclear Moment Data*, published by Isotope Analysis Methods Department, Oak Ridge National Laboratory, Oak Ridge, Tenn.
(ZW2)   G. D. Watkins and R. V. Pound, Phys. Rev., **85**, 1062 (1952).
(ZW3)   G. D. Watkins and R. V. Pound, Phys. Rev., **89**, 658 (1953).
(ZW4)   K. Way, Phys. Rev., **75**, 1448 (1949).
(ZW5)   R. T. Weidner, Phys. Rev., **72**, 1268 (1947).
(ZW5a) M. T. Weiss and M. W. P. Strandberg, Phys. Rev., **83**, 567 (1951).
(ZW6)   V. Weisskopf, Helv. Phys. Acta, **23**, 187 (1950); Science, **113**, 101 (1951).
(ZW7)   G. C. Wick, Z. Physik, **85**, 25 (1933); Nuovo cimento, **10**, 118 (1933).
(ZW8)   E. Wigner, Phys. Rev., **51**, 947 (1937).
(ZW9)   T. F. Wimett, private communication.
(ZW10) C. W. Wilson and G. E. Pake, J. Polymer Sci., **10**, 503 (1953); J. Chem. Phys. (1953).
(ZX1)   No complete or extensive references are here provided for the subject concerned.
(ZY1)   W. A. Yager and R. M. Bozorth, Phys. Rev., **72**, 80 (1947); **75**, 317 (1949).
(ZZ1)   E. J. Zavoisky, J. Phys. U.S.S.R., **10**, 197 (1946).
(ZZ2)   Zeiger, Bolef, and Rabi, Phys. Rev., **78**, 340 (1950).

Author Index

Subject Index

Subject Index 169